Years of Caring

Maurice W. White

To Doug Adams.

Maurice White

By the same author:

Brum and Candlelight

One Hundred Years of Learning:
Matthew Boulton College

Years of Caring

The Royal Orthopaedic Hospital

Maurice W. White

Brewin Books

First published October 1997 by
Brewin Books, Studley, Warwickshire.

© The Royal Orthopaedic Hospital
League of Friends 1997.

ISBN 1 85858 106 0
A British Library Cataloguing in Publication Data
Catalogue record for this book is available from
The British Library

Typeset in New Century Schoolbook
and made and printed in Great Britain
by Heron Press, Kings Norton, Birmingham

Years of Caring
The Royal Orthopaedic Hospital

The Woodlands
source: Royal Cripples Hospital Reports 1925-29
photo: Brian Jones

THE
ROYAL
ORTHOPÆDIC HOSPITAL
MEDICAL STAFF

SURGEONS		PHYSICIANS	
GEORGE FREER	1817-1829	Dr. DARWALL	1831-1853
MARTIN NOBLE SHIPTON	1821-1829	J. LLOYD	1833-1836
THOMAS FREER	1829-1879	Geo. FABIAN EVANS, M.D.	1833-1873
WALTER C. FREER, F.R.C.S.	1849-1912	T. WATKIN WILLIAMS, F.R.C.P.	1867-1883
CHARLES WARDEN, M.D., F.R.C.S.	1856-1912	T. BELL FLETCHER, M.D., F.R.C.P.	1873-1894
EDWARD LUKE FREER, M.R.C.S.	1879-1902	T. P. HESLOP, M.D., F.R.C.P.	1880-1895
Wm. THOMAS, M.D. (Lond.) F.R.C.S.	1883-1922	WALTER ROSS JORDAN, M.D. (Anaes)	1883-1933
GILBERT BARLING, F.R.C.S.	1884-1886	Jno. C. GRINLING, (Anaes)	1885-1899
AUGUSTUS F. CLAY	1886-1910	C.W. SUCKLING, M.D., M.R.C.P.	1886-1922
J. T. J. MORRISON, M.A., F.R.C.S.	1891-1896	H. GUY DAIN, LL.D.,M.D.(Hon) F.R.C.S.	1909-1948
W. EDWARD BENNETT, P.R.C.S.	1899-1919	E. WILSON HIRD, (Anaes)	1919-1925
W. DUNCAN LAWRIE, M.D., F.R.C.S.	1902-1909	T. L. HARDY, M.A., M.D., F.R.C.P.	1922-1929
FRANK BARNES, F.R.C.S.	1904-1918	J.F.BRAILSFORD, M.D.,Ph.D.,F.R.C.P.(Radio)	1923-1956
F. VICTOR MILWARD, F.R.C.S.	1908-1910	HELEN SCOTT MASON, (Anaes)	1925-1961
JORDAN LLOYD, F.R.C.S.	1908-1914	J.A.AINSCOW, (Anaes)	1926-1939
Chad. WOODWARD, F.R.C.S.	1910-1912	JAMES M. SMELLIE, M.A.,M.D.,F.R.C.P.	1930-1946
G. PERCIVAL MILLS, F.R.C.S.	1912-1946	L. KIRKBY THOMAS, (Anaes)	1934-1938
NAUGHTON DUNN, M.A., LL.D.	1913-1939	JANET R. WELSH, (Anaes)	1938-1967
J.B.LEATHER, M.A., F.R.C.S.	1916-1956	E. MARY FORSYTH, (Anaes)	1938-1970
F. WILSON STUART, M.D., Ch.M.	1917-1954	A. VICTOR NEALE, M.D., F.R.C.P.	1946-1947
F.G.ALLAN, F.R.C.S.	1939-1966	P. JACOBS, M.R.C.P., D.M.R.D.(Radio)	1955-1982
A.M.HENDRY, F.R.C.S.	1939-1963	PATRICIA M. LUMB, (Anaes) M.B.Ch.B.	1960-1968
T.S.DONOVAN, M.Ch.Orth., F.R.C.S.	1939-1966	M.R.C.S., L.R.C.P., D.A., F.F.A., R.C.S.,	
Wm. H. SCRASE, M.Ch.Orth.,F.R.C.S.	1956-1977	P. H. DENNISON, (Anaes) F.F.A., R.C.S.	1963-1988
M. H. M. HARRISON, Ch.M.,F.R.C.S.	1958-1985	G.HALL-DAVIES, F.F.A., R.C.S., D.A.	1968-
C.P.COTTERILL, M.Ch.Orth., F.R.C.S.	1963-1987	J.A.H. DAVIES, F.F.A., R.C.S., D.A.	1968-1992
H. PIGGOTT, F.R.C.S.	1963-1987	A. J. POPERT, M.D., M.B., B.S.	1964-1989
R.S. SNEATH, F.R.C.S.	1965-1993	F.R.C.P. (Lond)	
A.B.WATSON, F.R.C.S.	1965-1976	J.A.PROSSER, M.B., B.S.	1971-1990
J.N.COZENS-HARDY, F.R.C.S.	1965-1970	F.F.A.,R.C.S.(Eng)	
K.NORCROSS, F.R.C.S.	1966-1988		
J.R.PEARSON, F.R.C.S.	1966-1989		
J.A.JAMES, F.R.C.S. (Eng)	1958-1982		
R.L.BATTEN, F.R.C.S. (Eng)	1966-1982		
R.F. DUKE, F.R.C.S.(Eng)	1969-1986		
J.O'GARRA, F.R.C.S. (Ed)	1969-1988		

Medical Staff: Board 1

THE
ROYAL
ORTHOPÆDIC HOSPITAL
MEDICAL STAFF

SURGEONS

P.J. MULLIGAN, F.R.C.S. 1974–
A.G. THOMPSON, F.R.C.S. 1977–
O.N. TUBBS, F.R.C.S. 1978–
J.C.T. FAIRBANK, M.D., F.R.C.S. 1985–1989
D.J.W. Mc MINN, F.R.C.S. 1988–1994
R.J. GRIMER, F.R.C.S., F.R.C.S. Ed. 1988–
C. BRADISH, F.R.C.S. 1988–
A.J. STIRLING, F.R.C.S. 1990–
A.M.C. THOMAS, F.R.C.S. 1991–
S.R. CARTER, F.R.C.S. 1992–
M.A. WALDRAM, F.R.C.S. Ed. (Orth) 1993–
D.J.A. LEARMONTH B.Sc.,F.R.C.S. 1993–
J.J.L. PLEWES, F.R.C.S. 1993–
R.M. TILLMAN, F.R.C.S. 1994–
R.B.C. TREACY, F.R.C.S. (orth) 1994–
J.N. O'HARA, F.R.C.S. (orth) 1995–
D.S. MARKS, F.R.C.S.,F.R.C.S.(orth) 1996–
P.R. GLITHERO, F.R.C.S. Ed.(orth) 1996–

PHYSICIANS

N. EVANS, F.R.C.R. 1982–
A.M. DAVIES, D.M.R.D.,F.R.C.R.(Radio) 1984–
C.H. THOMAS, F.F.A., R.C.S. 1988–
T.D. NEAL, F.F.A., R.C.S. 1989–
D.M. HOWES, F.F.A. R.C.S. 1993–
I.D. GREEN, F.R.C.P. 1996–

Medical Staff: Board 2

3

This Book is Dedicated

to

John and Sandra

Contents

Michael H Bradbury

Foreword
by
Michael H. Cadbury
President of the League of Friends

This is a remarkable book about a remarkable institution. It covers a long and complete historical survey, and remains readable throughout with personal anecdotes and informed comments about the pioneers and current personalities.

The author Maurice White has used his literary experience to excellent effect. His research has been deep and wide. He has succeeded in catching the flavour of the struggles and successes over the years and conveys the friendly and welcoming atmosphere of the Hospital.

Opening with a valuable background to the Birmingham of 180 years ago when the social needs were not being met, he draws a picture of the recognition of a particular need and how it was gradually met.

The problems of finance, management and the ideals and caring philosophy of the founders are portrayed vividly.

One of the charms of the book is the constant reference to the people involved. This has been the success of the Woodlands. It has remained small enough to be a speciality unit where the whole staff can be aware of the rest of the team and somehow involve the patients in the overall caring professionalism and successful work of the doctors.

The growth from small private charity through amalgamation and takeover and now back to a self running Trust has had many crisis. Its constant forward looking to the latest pioneers of medicine and surgery has given it a unique place in the orthopaedic world. Its research, and training for doctors, nurses, physiotherapists and its school for young patients. The use of the hydrotherapy pool and its rural setting so near the heart of the midland conurbation are all part of its success.

The grateful thanks of the whole community goes out to the generous subscribers, to all the staff, and the volunteers of the League of Friends. We are sure the book will be welcomed by all connected with the Woodlands and hope by its sales that it will excite wider interest and further contributions to its finance.

Congratulations and thanks to its author Mr. Maurice White.

MHC.

June 1997.

Introduction

In writing this history it is my intention to give but a general overall picture of the development and growth of, primarily, the two major institutions that on amalgamating in 1925, led to the Royal Orthopaedic Hospital as we know it today. It would be impossible to produce a detailed history. My main sources of information come directly from the Minute Books, copiously written by hand, and Annual Reports. Such information is history in its own right offering a glimpse into actual events as they occur. The material being enclosed in a story line, and generalising over periods of time.

There occur a number of 'offshoots' which to some extent are peripheral to the main story, however they are of such interest that I have separated them out, as additional sections.

The Orthopaedic movement from 1817, and the Crippled Children's Union from 1896, is followed by Amalgamation then a further 23 years to the start of the National Health Service in 1948, under the umbrella of the Royal Cripples Hospital (from 1927), the Royal Orthopaedic title then returning. Many administrative changes, take place over the next 45 years, the Hospital being grouped, initially, with 11 others, under control of the Birmingham (Selly Oak) Management Committee, during which period there were, unsuccessful, attempts to split up the Woodlands onto other sites. The 1970s brought in to being the League of Friends, and the early 1990s was certainly a watershed, a fight for survival, won by the determination that "The Woodlands was not to be closed". and so the story ends, or rather begins, with the formation of The Royal Orthopaedic NHS Trust.

This is not a medical journal, but about people and events. Which way would the history have gone without the benevolence of Mr. George Cadbury? In what direction would the crippled children's plight have moved without the energy of Mr. Frank Mathews? What contributions did Mr. A.E.Wort and Mr. H.F.Harvey play? And about the numerous men and women, whose initiatives and efforts, have made the Royal Orthopaedic

Hospital what it is today. As the history will show, there is nothing new, gardens were being tended at the Newhall Street Hospital 100 years ago; fund raising and tours of the Woodlands over 80 years ago. Sadly hospitals have gone, 'Forelands'; 'Broad Street', to name but two.

The chapter of 'Memories' provides so many views of life in the hospitals' from former staff and, most touchingly, from people who had spent so many years of their young lives there, expressed most vividly, in many cases, as through the eyes of children. All of which praise the staff for their caring attitudes.

Little has changed as we go into the 21st Century but the titles of the institutions as the hospital has grown from its humble beginnings in 1817 to being in 1997 :-

"The Royal Orthopaedic Hospital NHS Trust the pre-eminent Orthopaedic Service in the West Midlands ".

The 'Woodlands' is, and always will be, the 'Caring Hospital'.

Maurice W. White.
June 1997.

Setting the Scene

THE GENERAL HOSPITAL, or at least the shell of it, which is a plain, but noble edifice, was erected in 1766, upon a situation very unsuited to its elegant front, being a dirty lane with an aspect directing up the hill; which should ever be avoided. The two wings were added in 1791, at the expense of £3016. It is supported by voluntary subscriptions. A music meeting is also held once in three years, and the manager of the Theatre gives an annual benefit, to add to its funds; ... frequent large requests find their way to this valuable institution. Hundreds recover health and strength there, which otherwise might perish. Many of the physicians and surgeons of the town give their attendance and assistance gratis, and it is impossible to discover a place where more humanity is shown.

This description of the, then, town of Birmingham's first Hospital (standing in Summer Lane at the foot of Snow Hill), is taken, <u>exactly</u> as written, from 'A Brief History of Birmingham: Intended as A Guide To The Inhabitant & Stranger, 1805'.

"The return in 1801, under the population act, of the number of families, houses, etc., within the parish is as follows:- houses inhabited, 12,044, families, 12,683, males, 28,568, females, 32,254, total of inhabitants, 60,822. In the out-parts, including Deritend, Bordesley, etc. the return is, houses inhabited, 1,017, males, 2,392, females, 2,629. Ashted, Duddeston, etc. houses inhabited, 739, males, 1,706, females, 1,835. Total inhabitants of the hamlets, 8,562; making the total number of inhabitants in the connected streets and houses, 69,384".

Now to proceed to the rapid movement toward a much wider field of medical needs. The General Hospital having overcome its struggling position of the 1770s, had taken some twelve years from 1766, following its foundation by John Ash, (on whose death the suburb of Ashted was named), to raise sufficient funds to finally open and run wards, (the music meeting, held once every three years, mentioned in the introductory paragraph was the forerunner of the Triennial Music Festivals held in Birmingham for many years). The Hospital's success is clear by 1805. It was not however alone, for in 1792 there "... is agitation to establish a Dispensary ...".

* "February 11th, 1792. This laudable institution originated amongst a select society ... carried on in a private manner ... until joined by Mr. Matthew Boulton Esq. (of Soho fame), who took it under his patronage in 1793 when a House was taken in Temple Row, and an establishment formed. It continued in Temple Row, supported by Voluntary Subscriptions and donations, until the year 1808".

"The first annual report was presented at a meeting held November 7th, 1794. ... 325 patients had received medical advice and assistance at their own homes, of which 246 were sick patients, 48 Midwifery and 31 inoculation patients. That the encouragement given to the institution, and the peculiar benefits given to the poor, had been such as to have determined the Committee to take a house and engage an apothecary, whose whole time should be devoted to the service of the charity".

The house in Temple Row was soon found to be inadequate ... and in 1806 a subscription was opened for the purpose of opening a more commodious building.

* J.A.Langford 'A Century of Birmingham Life' Vol. 2. 1791-1841.

On December 1st, it is stated ... 'Our ingenious townsman Mr. W. Hollins, has finished a drawing of the intended new building for the Dispensary'. In the Gazette (Aris's Birmingham Gazette) of the following week the additional information is given:-

DISPENSARY

December 15th. 1806. The friends of this valuable institution will be happy to see such a respectable list of Subscribers to the new building about to be erected in this town for the purpose of the Charity. ... and we trust that within a week we shall find the number considerably increased in order to enable the Committee not only to provide an attached dwelling house for the mid-wifery attendants, but to administer those comforts to the poor women of this class of patients of which they so frequently stand in need, and which the scanty funds of the institution have hitherto prevented the Committee from supplying.

"The new building was opened in 1808 and during the year which ended

December 31st, 1866, 7,100 sick patients, and 356 midwifery patients received medical and surgical aid, and 1,169 vaccinations were performed. The total number of patients from the foundation of the Institution in 1793 to 1866 was 328,312, divided into 196,834 sick, 36,035 midwifery, and 95,413 vaccinations; a splendid record of services rendered to suffering humanity by the Birmingham Dispensary".

Many changes had taken place in the town of Birmingham in the early 19th Century. There were, primarily, but the two establishments; The General Hospital, not itself in a particularly salubrious part of the town, 'that dirty lane, with an aspect directing up the hill, which should ever be avoided', being hardly a welcoming invitation.

The Birmingham Dispensary, was certainly more central and convenient in Union Street. Its position was a site on the right hand side of Union Street, going up from High Street, between today's Martineau Way and Corporation Street. There was no Corporation Street at that time, and in fact Joseph Chamberlain's dream of a Boulevard, from New Street through to Gosta Green, was very much intended to improve the health of the town's inhabitants, by clearing 'one of the oldest and most unhealthy parts of the town'. This was some 70 years ahead, so even the conditions ambient to the Dispensary were far from ideal.

At no time has the need for the plight of the Physically Deformed been mentioned in the 50 years since the foundation of the General Hospital in 1766.

1817 was therefore a major turning point, for this year witnessed the establishment of an Orthopaedic Hospital. The plight of the cases of "Bodily Deformity" was about to be addressed, with the founding of the:-

General Institute for the Relief of Bodily Deformities on
Tuesday 24th day of June, 1817.

The important facts one would expect to have been taken into consideration at the setting up of a new hospital must surely be to have seen the Committee building on the experiences of the existing institutions, particularly since the surgeons and physicians spread their services across the board. Even more relevant would be their method of raising funds, primarily from subscriptions (a ticket system) and donations. The very same sources that had provided funds before 1817 which at times, were found wanting by the other institutions, were now to be tapped for more; for them to dig even further into their, not so deep, pockets.

It is not surprising to find that matters did not improve, either in terms of income for the Orthopaedic Hospital, or living conditions in the town, which in turn meant even greater income required by the Institutions. The population of nearly 70,000 in 1801 had increased to some 90,000 by 1817, many of whom were living in squalid courts and yards.

This was the situation facing the New Orthopaedic Hospital.

Chapter 1

1817 - 1925
The Orthopaedic Institutions

With the Right Honourable the Earl of Dartmouth in the chair the Meeting was held, on Tuesday 17 th June 1817, (No venue is stated), for the purpose of considering the 'Propriety of establishing an Institution for the Relief of Persons labouring under Bodily Deformity' The outline of the deliberations being " To take into consideration the great Difficulty of obtaining advice and Relief in Cases of Bodily Deformity, and being of Opinion that it would be desirable to promote an Institution for the Purpose of Relieving those who labour under such deformity, either natural or accidental, and who have not the Means of Procuring Advice and Instruments properly adapted to their unfortunate Situation; and taking into Consideration also, the prevalence of Hernia Complaints; do now Resolve to establish a Society for such Charitable Purposes, to be called, "The General Institution for the Relief of Persons labouring under Bodily Deformity."

The Earl of Dartmouth was appointed Patron, Mr.Freer, Surgeon, and Mr. John Welchman Whately, Secretary.

The list of the Gentlemen attending is truly a veritable ' Whose Who' of Birmingham Men of the Day.

Heneage Legge; Francis Lawley; F.B.Hacket; Isaac Spooner

Charles Lloyd; Tertius Galton; Rev. A.E.Bagot; Rev. T.L.Freer

A.S.Lillington; John Rotton; Rev. J.H.Spry; Rev. J.Kentish

R. Spooner; Theodore Price; Dr. John Johnstone; James Taylor

Dr. De Lys; James Lloyd; Timothy Smith; Dr. Booth; David Lloyd

Thomas Potts; J Pearson; P. M. James. and J. Scholefield.

The first official committee meeting took place on Friday the 4th July, at which it was agreed that the Resolutions, as previously passed, together with a list of Subscribers should be advertised in the Birmingham, Warwick and Provincial Papers. (Aris's Gazette, Birmingham's oldest newspaper, had already run a detailed article).

Mr. Freer stated that he had engaged a House in New Street lately in the occupation of ? Davis, at a Yearly rental of £31-10s, and had circulated 500 printed copies of the Resolutions, with a list of Subscribers. A search of the Parish of Birmingham Levy Book for New Street, for 1816-21 failed to conclusively identify this property. Three facts found however were: Mr. Freer, himself lived at 36 New Street (the, then, Theatre Royal was No.72); Freer, Rotton, Lloyd & Co were at 91, and No. 80 New Street was a 'handsome House and Building, Thomas Davis was Landlord and it was rated at £31-0s-0d'. This could fit the bill.

The August meeting, set out the proposed Subscriber's ticket system. Annual Subscriber's of:- 1 guinea can recommend 2 patients for Rupture; 2 guineas, 4 patients for Rupture and 1 for Bodily Deformity; 10 guineas and upwards, at any one time, the same as 1 guinea subscribers,during the life of the donor. Similarly 20 guineas, same as for 2 guineas, for life, and so on. (This ticket system, passing through numerous modifications, was to continue for 109 years).

The following month Mr. George Freer reports the first statistics, but highlights early problems of communication. 15 patients for Instruments and Deformity; 10 patients for Trusses. However 15 people had been turned away, having attended without recommendation. Additional publicity was necessary together with a need for more subscribers, in order to extend it's benefits.

Other than through the newspapers, how were subscribers to be solicited? Here the Committee had to organise its members and divide the town into seven districts. Messrs Russell; Taylor; Lloyd; Pearson; Potts; Scholefield; Simcox; Price; Galton; Lee; Rev. Howells; Saunders; Rev. Freer; Haughton, covering, in pairs respectively: Moseley & Sparkhill; Newhall Street & St. Paul's; Bull Street & St. Mary's; Suffolk Street & Islington; (Five Ways); The Foreign Districts (Digbeth/Deritend); Dale End & Ashted; and Handsworth District.

A novel source of advertising announced, soon used, was to send copies of the resolutions and lists of subscribers to 'all Lodging Houses opened for the reception of strangers and to principal visitors to the town'

Over the 18 months, Summer 1817 to December 1818, business had flourished, with 181 cases of Ruptures and 87 Bodily Deformity. Unfortunately income had not. 'Subscriptions were found to be quite inadequate to meet expenditure.' Long gaps in the 'Minutes' were ominous (to the Author) and at the end of December 1820, George Freer announced his resignation, which he withdrew a month later when Mr. Martin Noble Shipton (a former pupil of Mr. Freer) offered his services, resulting in Freer and Shipton being appointed Joint Surgeons. However it came to light that "...for unavoidable circumstances, the Institute has for some-time been nearly suspended..."

A rallying call declaring the full conviction of the Committee and its success in bringing relief to a mass of patients, gave the necessary impetus for increased support.

Four years later some light is shed on the New Street facilities, when Mr. Shipton announces his intention of removing his Surgery and Residence. "... the shops etc. of this Institution, be like-wise removed to Mr. Shipton's house ...". Again no address is given.

Over the ensuing years income was still not covering expenditure, Committee members were being asked to solicit Annual subscriptions among their friends to discharge arrears, and the Rev. Kentish offered to preach a Sermon at St. Philip's Church on the Institutes behalf. There is a 4 year gap in the Minutes 1825-29., and in the September Mr. Shipton resigns (leaving Birmingham) being replaced by Mr. Thomas Freer. The "shop heretofore used for making the Instruments and Trusses is to be continued for one year"

A Dr. Darnell and Mr. Freer (presumably Thomas) receive thanks for their gratuitous service and a Dr. Lloyd enters as Physician, however he was replaced in 1836 by Dr. Evans. Moving on to 1841 we meet the Instrument maker. ' T. W.' is no longer to be employed at weekly wages, but paid for each instrument he makes. Three years later T. W. is asked to "attend at the Institution daily at the time appointed by the Medical Officers ... and that he be paid 18 shillings a week and a commission of one shilling in the pound for all subscriptions he collects". All seems well for a while.

Another surgeon Dr. MacKay is taken on to relieve the pressures on Mr. Freer. At an Annual meeting of Subscribers held in July 1845 T.W. is warned regarding his punctuality and reprimanded "... appointment to be cancelled unless satisfaction within 3 months ..." At the end of that period the Medical Officers reported "...that they have experienced the greatest inconvenience from the neglect of T.W. in supplying the patients with instruments. That he be dismissed ...". An alternative outside source for the supply of Trusses and Instruments was authorised "... on the most advantageous terms possible ...", and the shop closed.

Letters of resignation were received from Dr. MacKay and Mr. Freer in 1849, the latter having given 24 years service accepting the Office of Consultant. Mr. Walter Carless Freer and Mr. William Cockerell were appointed as Surgeons. Dr. Charles Warden who was to play a leading role for the next 50 years, was appointed Surgeon, in 1856.

On the 40th Anniversary of the Institute, a change of premises was announced, but with an immediate warning. "... The premises recently taken in Great Charles Street, are centrally situated, convenient for the attendances of patients, admirably adapted for the required purposes, but the Committee look forward, and venture to hope that, erelong, by the liberality of the Public, to engage larger premises, where they can have a few beds." Is this the first move towards an Inpatient Department?

A name change is declared, expanding on the treatments being offered, and spreading the geographic boundaries, together with revision of rules.

'The Birmingham and Midland Counties Orthopaedic Institution,

for the Cure of Hernia, Club Foot, Spinal Diseases, Contractions and Distortions of Limbs and all Bodily Deformities.'

The Medical Staff was to consist of a Consulting Physician, Consulting Surgeon and 2 Honorary Surgeons. The Physician practicing as a pure Physician or Surgeon. A 'Collector' was to be appointed "... to devote his time to canvassing for new subscriptions ..." 40 years before, 14 men had this task!.

Annual Subscribers of £1-1-0 were now to recommend 6 patients for trusses for Hernia, or 1 patient requiring supports for the Spine, or instruments for deformed limbs, whilst a Donation of £10-10, constituted a

Life Governor, still with the privilege of annual subscriber for 10 years. This latter also applied to Overseers to the Poor; Treasurers of Charity Schools; Stewards or Secretaries of Sick Clubs and Benefit Societies.

Patient Regulations included, Gratuitous advice from Hon. Surgeons to the deformed poor, every Monday and Thursday at 2 o'clock. Urgent cases admitted without letters of recommendation, but if instruments are required tickets must be obtained. Patients unable to walk shall be attended at home. Patients absenting themselves more than 14 days shall be discharged.

At the Annual Meeting of 1862 an increase in Subscriptions was reported,(but again a warning sign is given) from £74 to £92 and Donations £90 to £125, including the handsome sum of £107-6s-8d from the local charities, without which the Operations of the Society must have been grievously crippled. The moral rallying call follows; "... there are 50 children born annually in the town, with club feet, each one costs in instruments alone, £2 and requires almost constant attention for at least a year. But this year we will send forth 50 human beings who instead of being cripples will, in the majority of cases, have no evidences of their deformity remaining. ... without being too sanguine we hope to see subscriptions doubled this year ..."

Two years later concern is being expressed over the share of income being received from the Amalgamated Charities Fund. An appeal was sent " ... that the claims of this Institution had not been sufficiently recognised ... to make an appeal through the Clergy and Ministers, to their respective Congregations for special donations. ... The Committee cannot fail to be disappointed that our Charity doing so much good, in so important class of cases, and requiring such expensive treatment, should have been placed in the lowest class."

Dr. Warden's Medical report given at the next Annual Meeting sets out his reasoning as to two causes for the prevalence of Bodily Deformity. "... the almost exclusive use of white instead of brown bread, and the adulteration of bread with Alum. The husk of the corn was bone-forming and bone-nourishing. Hardly any husk remained in the flour of which white bread was made and that little was converted by Alum into a substance that was incapable of assimilation in the body ... In white bread there was no bone-building substance whatsoever. The bones being deprived of proper nourishment became soft and yielded to the pressure of the body. People ought to eat brown bread".

Needless to say the Mill Owners rejected the charge, but did say that "... only obscure men adulterated bread with Alum ... and they will soon be wholly put to an end if people would not thoughtlessly look for nice looking loaves, without regard to anything beyond appearances...".

The Golden Jubilee Meeting was held at the Midland Institute, (then in Paradise Street) at which a Jubilee Fund was communicated, 30 guineas being promised in the room. The Right Honourable the Lord Dartmouth had held the Presidency from the opening of the Institution, but in July 1868 the Committee sadly records " ... that a vote of condolence be rendered to Lord Calthorpe on the Death of his father, and that he be respectfully requested to accept the Office of Patron so long and kindly held by his lamented father. ...".

A subsequent request for an increased Rent for the Hospital, with conditions, left the Committee with little choice; " ... An application having been made by the Proprietor of the Hospital, for an increased Rent, he having been solicited to let the premises for the purpose of Public Vaccination, and which is deemed inadvisable ...". His request was acceded to, £10 being added to the Rent.

The Right Revd. the Lord Bishop of Worcester was appointed to fill the Office of President, at the 52nd Annual Meeting. Lord Dartmouth being added to the List of Patrons.

An improved income from Charities came in November 1871, with the mention of the Hospital Sunday Fund; "... handsome Donation received from the Periodical Collections on 'Hospital Sunday' ... the sum of £282-13s."(the Hospital Sunday Fund was *founded in 1859, being a simultaneous appeal in all the churches and chapels in Birmingham and the neighbourhood, on behalf of the medical charities. *Reference Robert K. Dent's, Making of Birmingham. 1894. page 553).

Initially this was received tri-Annually.

In the Spring of 1872, the committee is looking for new premises, Dr.

Warden having communicated that he had the 'second refuse' of premises in Broad Street, suitable for the purposes of the Hospital. (not the Broad Street Hospital we know, that was some 50 years ahead.)

Spirits were dashed when 6 months later, the owners had " declined to let their premises for the purpose of the hospital". Again in April 1873, the Tenancy of another property, on the corner of Edmund Street and Congreve Street was offered, which was turned down as "... the expense that could be incurred in carrying out alterations and repairs, coupled with the uncertainty of the tenancy, was more than the premises were worth.". October of 1874 marks another attempt, a saga which runs for some 9 months. The site, the old Homoeopathic Hospital, on the Upper Priory side of the Old Square. An offer was made of £120 pa. on a 21 year lease. The Landlord responded, offering additional houses, including a coffee-house, at a greater cost. The Committee's Architects commenting on the state of the Window frames; flooring and generally rotten woodwork suggested complete demolition.

However in December 1874 they increased their offer to £150 pa. to no avail. By April 1875 the site is up for Auction, and (amazingly) the Hon.Sec. is instructed to attend and bid up to £5,000. Eight days later "... if the Hon. Sec. can acquire the Property for a sum not exceeding £3,500, he be empowered to close the matter." Two days later the figure of £4,000 is stated as being the lowest acceptable, (including a piece of land at the back), resulted in the Committee going to £3,800. This was not accepted, whence the end of the attempt.

Meanwhile the hospital, in Great Charles Street, was still running, the total income for the year 1875 was £660, total expenditure £443, of which £250 was spent on instruments and medicine, only £92 for all other expenses including Rent, salaries, printing etc. Dr. Charles Warden stated that 759 cases had been treated; 3,757 had attended; 506 cured; 189 relieved; 61 remained under treatment; 248 patients coming from surrounding districts. Despite the above failed negotiations, or perhaps because of them, he called for a 'new building and accommodation'.

By November 1876, the committee is looking at the possibility of extensions at the current site, by securing "... the wing of an adjacent building ...". in order to add a few beds to the hospital. " ... as it would give them all the accommodation needed for some years to come ... and a much needed convenience of a Dispensary on the Premises ...". The Landlord was contacted to ascertain if, and on what terms he would be willing to grant an extension on the Lease.

The content of the letter sent included the statement "... Having had it examined by an Architect and plans prepared, they now learn that it is in such a state of decay that nothing less than pulling down and rebuilding, will render it in the least suitable for their requirements ... and that as it will cause an outlay of at least £300, they feel they are not justified in incurring so large an expense while merely tenants ...".

The reply came "... I regret that I am unable to meet the visions of the committee of the Orthopaedic Hospital, by granting to them a Lease of the premises in Great Charles Street, which they occupy as yearly tenants ...".

The Committee, undaunted, continued their searches, and, presumably with the view of sharing costs:- "... the Hon. Sec be instructed to Communicate with the Committees of Minor Charities, with a view to Amalgamation ...".

That search for new premises ended, 'just around the corner' when on the 31st July 1877 "... An offer had been received of Premises now occupied by the Civil Engineers in Newhall Street" (No.81, at the junction with Great Charles Street). and 3 weeks later "... that the Premises recently occupied by the Mechanical Engineers (obviously incorrectly named in the previous 'minute') could be had immediately, that the Rent would be £90 pa. and in all probability a lease of 7 or 14 years would be had ...".

A special meeting of the Committee held in September resolved unanimously "... that so manifestly advantageous offer should not be allowed to slip. Having also in view that probably the Ear and Throat Infirmary, may amalgamate under the same roof and so reduce the General Expenditure ...". One month later the hospital took possession on Michaelmas day. An appeal was made for funds to assist with the fitting up and furnishing, resulting in Donations amounting to -

£526-15s, and new Annual Subscriptions of £47-5-0. The Removal was effected during Christmas week and on the 31st December 1877 the New

Hospital opened for the reception of Patients, and the Ear and Throat Infirmary became sub-tenants.

In January 1878 we meet the first, named, Matron, it being "... recommended that Miss U. Dorrell of the Wylie Farm, *Heightington, be elected Matron, at a salary of £30 pa." she was to take up her duties from the end of February. *In Hereford & Worcester near Bliss Gate.

A suggestion that inpatients should pay 10/6d per week in advance, was made by Mr. Freer, entitling them to remain in Hospital for one-week, a Book of Tickets to be printed for that purpose. Also a payment was to be made of 5/- by any Medical Officer using a 'Sayer's Spinal Apparatus'. Mr. Freer himself presented to the Institution a 'Set of Sayer's Pulleys' with Cross Bar and Pulley for the extension of the lower extremities. It was also resolved, in May 1878, that 5/- for 2 days be paid for one inpatient ticket.

Five years after its foundation, the Saturday Hospital Fund, is recorded in a Minute of 14th June 1878, as giving £40-6-8d to the Hospital. (*The Founder of this movement, was Joseph Sampson Gamgee, a distinguished Surgeon, in 1869, in connection with the, then, Queen's Hospital [Bath Row]. Hospital Saturday being simultaneous appeals in the various manufactories and workshops of the, then, Town). *Reference; 'Making of Birmingham, by Robert K. Dent. 1891', and ,'1873-1973 The Golden Years, A Concise History of the Birmingham Hospital Saturday Fund', by Mr. E. R. Sherlock.

An unusual and valuable present of 'a bundle of firewood' was made by a Mr. Amos Roe, followed by a 'handsome, donation of Pen and Pen holders' by Messrs. Gillott.

Six months on, from the opening of the new hospital, the share of costs by the Ear and Throat Infirmary was agreed as being " ... £25 for their share of the 'signs' ... a sum of £17, less £2 allowed for Drugs, be paid as their share for fitting up the Dispensary, and that future expenses be met in equal proportions".

A Mrs. Smith, having furnished a bed, intending to present it to the Hospital in August 1878, appears to mark the beginning of 'bed donations'. And only 10 months after the opening of the new premises, Dr. Warden is again stating successful statistics. "... By March, twenty patients could be accommodated at one time; 147 had already been admitted; £200 had been received from the William Dudley Trust; In the period July 1877 to June 1878; 1,100 admitted (387 being from surrounding districts); 7,435 attendances; 825 cured; 182 greatly relieved; 93 under treatment. Of the 147 inpatients, 25 Spinal Jackets, remainder Club feet, Hip diseases and other deformities; 512 instruments of various kinds used at a cost of £369-8s. Medicine had also been administered, at very considerable cost, and on the free system, without tickets and admission notes of any kind ".

The death of Thomas Freer, Hon. Consultant Surgeon, was noted March 1879, being succeeded by Mr. D. W. Crompton. Another appeal is made in September 1879, for a greater share of charitable funding, this time to the Sunday Hospital Fund. "... At a meeting of the committee ... the proportion of the fund appropriated to this Hospital was taken into consideration ... The Hospital is now accommodating a large number of patients, 418 in the past year, and its expenditure is at least trebled since the opening of the inpatient department. Its income has not increased with its expenses and the Committee venture to hope that a claim is considered for a larger proportion in the distribution of the Funds than hitherto and that the Charity will be placed in a higher class in the forthcoming division".

One example of a country patient is seen with this letter from a potential subscribers, 'Union Offices, Ludlow':- "... I am directed by the Guardians to inform you they have much pleasure in becoming Annual Subscribers and forward a cheque for £2-2-0. and that there is a child aged 7 years with a very weak ankle now in the Workhouse, and the Guardians are desirous that she should be sent to your Hospital, but she cannot leave the house just at present. ... will it be necessary for me to write to you before sending her?"

Mr. John Warden Browett Hon. Sec. of the Hospital states the Ground Rules for prospective Applicants for the Medical Staff; Candidates must possess either Membership or Fellowship of the College of Surgeons of London, Edinburgh or Dublin, and the Election be decided by the Majority of the Committee of the Hospital. Another member of the Freer family subsequently takes his place with the appointment of Mr. Edward L. Freer, as Assistant Honorary Surgeon in December 1879. Two months later Dr.

Thomas P. Heslop is appointed Hon. Consultant Physician.

Voluntary workers were in action in the 1880's. as seen , when 'a special vote of thanks' was given to the 'Ladies of the Flower Mission for their kind contribution of Flowers to the Institution'. Sadly there was not as yet a need for 'gardeners'. However the question of laying out the garden, (in Newhall Street!), was a matter left in the hands of the Committee Chairman, he being authorised to spend the sum of £10.

In July 1880 the share of the Saturday Hospital Fund was £104-3-3d, and the death is announced of Dr. Miller "... whose services to this Institution, were most earnest, constant and valuable...". (this was probably the former Canon Miller, the then Rector of St. Martin's-in-the-Bull Ring, whose exertions had resulted in the founding of the Sunday Hospital Fund, in 1859). The Newhall Street Hospital was to give support to the District Nursing Society, by offering the use of its Board Room. One's imagination could run wild at the following development, when in August "... a sub-committee was appointed to make arrangements for a Bath and the necessary Hot and Cold Water connections". The need for a 'Safe', and a 'Rug' for the Consulting Room was also essential.

The next Annual Meeting states that " ... the Lord Newport of Castle Bromwich be invited to accept the Office of President for the ensuing year". At this period the hospital title is ' The Orthopaedic and Spinal Hospital and Ear and Throat Infirmary'

In early 1881 another donation in kind is received '2 guineas worth of Potatoes, from Mr. Benjamin Hartley, Potato Merchant, Curzon Street, Birmingham'. 4 months later; "... the question of cleaning and papering the hospital, be left to a sub-committee; A Donation of £2-2-0 is received from the Birmingham and District Football Association; A Donation of Books from the Misses Simpson (start of a Library?), and , a Parcel of Linen was announced as having been given by Mrs. Gottwaltz, late of Handsworth. (a Mrs. Gottwalz ran the Old Post Office opposite to the Theatre Royal, and close to the site of the Orthopaedic House, in the early part of the nineteenth Century).

The apportionment of the Drug Account between the two institutions, is revised. "... paid at the rate of 2/3 for the Ear and Throat, and 1/3 for the

Orthopaedic, as the ascertained facts proved that it was about the proportions used by each. 6 months on and the ' Bath minute, was continued'. The question of the Nurse having been considered, it was deemed advisable to appoint a Servant to do the general housework. The Matron being instructed to appoint a suitable person at a salary not exceeding £12 pa. That nurses be provided with dresses suitable to their Offices and an easy chair or sofa provided for Matron's Sitting Room.

And now, at last, in September 1881 "... it was decided a No. 2 Ewart's Crown Boiler be obtained at the cost of £9-9-0, and a Bath be erected in connection with it, in the Closet upon the 2nd Landing". At the 1881 Annual Meeting, the Most Noble the Marquess of Hertford becomes the President. A very unsatisfactory state of Finances is reported and concern is expressed at the disproportionate subscriptions being received from country areas in relation to the numbers attending. Mr. Morris is appointed Dispenser at a salary of £40 pa. early 1882. Domestically, an outside agency is seen to have been helping out, "... a vote of thanks being given, to the Domestic of the Nurses Training Institute for services at the Hospital." Some change has also been made, with a decision to take on an Assistant General Servant at wages not exceeding £7 pa. and that in the future the post of Charwoman be discontinued.

On the 22nd of December 1882, "... discussion arose on the advisability of appointing an Assistant Physician with the Special view of taking charge of the use of Chloroform". No decision was made, the Special Meeting adjourned and the matter left in the hands of the Hon. Surgeons to exercise their discretion, and call in a Practical Chloroformist if needed.

The following item identifies an outside source 'In Aid of the Funds of the Institution', and gives a flavour of some Historical fact of the day. The 'Minute' statement of 23rd January 1883, says:- "... received a cheque for £43-12-5 less £6-16-0, from the Ladies and Gentlemen who gave the Entertainment in Aid of the Funds ... following an Amateur Dramatic Entertainment at the ' Bijou' Theatre on Friday 10th November 1882. Mr. Patrick Baird, Head of the Social and Local Studies sections at Birmingham Central Reference Library kindly searched out an 1872 programme for the Bijou Palace of Minstrelsy. - St. James Hall - opposite the Great Western Station, Snow Hill. Kelly's Directory shows that it was at No. 14 Snow Hill (right hand side going down from Colmore Circus) in existence from 1868. Victor J. Price in his book "Birmingham Theatres" further states that in 1913 it was the Egyptian Hall Billiard Room.

Mr. William Thomas is appointed Honorary Surgeon, March 1883, he was to be one of the surgeons to the Cripple's Union, in some 15 years ahead, and in the following May, Mr. Ross Jordan appointed to the post of Chloroformist. Improved communication is being considered with the erection of Telephone wires, in the hospital, "... on certain conditions ..."! whatever that may mean.

January 1884 saw the commencement of Mr. Thorneywork's long association as Instrument maker to the hospital. His Tender being for; ' Scarpers; Leg Irons; Chin Slings; Plain Special Instruments; Poro Plastic Jackets; Jury Masks; Crutches; Patterns; Boots etc. His duties being that he attend daily at 2 o'clock to receive instructions from the Surgeon. This year again found the hospital in need of funds, sufficiently serious as to deem it necessary to send out a circular signed by the President. "... only £100 in Legacies had been received, as against £500 last year ...". Another considerable loss being that the Ear and Throat Infirmary having moved out, there was great anxiety as how to recoup the resulting loss of £100 pa. Rent.

Phrasing of Minute entries, of the day, can give wrong impressions. "... Expressed sorrow at the loss of Mr. Walter C. Freer, in the active work of the Charity, having held Office of Surgeon for 40 years ...". Have no fear however, he had not died, "... we now avail of his good counsel and advice as Consulting Surgeon ...".

An update as to the Medical Officers in 1875, introduces a most important man, for in addition to Hon. Consulting Physician; T. Bell Fletcher; Consulting Surgeons; D.W.Crompton and W.C.Freer; Surgeons; Chas. Warden; E.L.Freer; W.Thomas; we meet as Assistant Surgeon; Gilbert Barling. who was to play a prominent role in Amalgamation in the 1920's. The Anaesthetist is Jno. C. Grinley.

The following year an additional Assistant Surgeon is Augustas F. Clay. In order to promote financial support "... a gentleman being engaged who travelled for 3 months, visiting the principal towns within a 30 mile radius of the hospital...". The resulting Donations of £64-17-6d, and £21-8-6d Subscriptions, were pure income as the whole venture was borne by 'no less a personage than' Mr. John H. Chance.

What about a Mortuary? The Committee "...think it proper to bring to your attention the great necessity that has arisen for a proper mortuary ... considering the large number of cases ... the death rate is extremely light ..." The Committee having no suitable building, were not able to justify further debt upon ground which is under annual tenancy. A perhaps more surprising need is that of a 'more efficient Bath, the one in use being quite inadequate'. Despite the previous installation it was clearly unsuitable for '... proper cleansing of children and adults ...'. The matter is raised again at the 1887 Annual Meeting together with a warning to subscribers. "... Sanitary conditions are not satisfactory ... £500 would have to be expended ... It is therefore for you to decide whether the necessary improvements shall take place, and if so, to put them in possession of the necessary funds.".

The committee then projects an anticipated greater outlay, in that that appeal although related to the existing hospital building, embracing, in addition, new wards; operating theatres; increased sleeping accommodation for staff, that it would prefer expending a sum of £2,500 to £3,000 in erecting a new building on another site.

A Convalescent home had been used during 1888, Captain and Mrs Grice Hutchinson of Chambers Court, Tewkesbury, having offered a furnished house at, nearby, Longden. 16 children having received the benefits, under the care of a trained hospital matron and the supervision of Mrs Grice Hutchinson. On the 28th July 1888 a Memorial Stone was laid by the Marquess of Hertford. (this relating to the addition of a new-wing at Newhall Street) and a sum of £61-15-11d, together with a cheque for £50, given by Her Most Gracious Majesty, Queen Victoria, was 'laid' on the Stone. A declaration that "... new building is now covered in ... it is hoped that it will be completed by Christmas ..." carries the good news "... without any addition to the debts at present resting on the institution ...". The public are now invited to 'endow beds'.

That new-wing was opened in May 1889, the actual cost being £1,128-10-3d. In December 1888 "... Her Most Gracious Majesty the Queen, gave her Royal Permission to your Committee to use the Title 'Royal' in the name, which is now named the Royal Orthopaedic and Spinal Hospital". this event coincides with the conferring of 'City' Status on Birmingham.

November 1888 had marked an outbreak of Scarlet Fever in the Hospital, resulting in the need to close the inpatient department for disinfection. The death of a most local worthy, came with the announcement of the passing of Miss Louisa Ann Ryland "... so munificent a Donor to all Birmingham Charities ...". (Cannon Hill and Victoria [Small Heath] Parks being amongst her gifts).

Mr. J.T.Morrison is appointed Assistant Surgeon in 1891 and although a £38 increase had been received in subscriptions as a result of the hospital enlargement, expenditure had increased by £268. The call goes out again, increased accommodation, increased waiting lists (what is new!), the institution not sufficiently large to cope with the demands made upon it, appealing for further financial aid. Mr. E.Luke Freer has moved to Llandudno opening a convalescent home in connection with the hospital.

The 1st May 1891 was observed at the Hospital as the First 'Pound Day', a day on which friends of the Charity were invited to visit the hospital and bring a Pound of something useful. The result being very satisfactory, large quantities of groceries being brought in. Agreed that this should be an annual May Day event. Miss Burgess has been appointed Matron (a hospital trained nurse) and two probationers from the Birmingham and Midland Counties Training Institution for Nurses, whose services are obtained free in return for their training. These moves ensuring for inpatients careful nursing at nights as well as day-time.

Improvements have been made in the Hospital, additional windows, raising ceilings, increased ventilation producing more cheerful and sanitary conditions through purer air. Wards, and the Operating Theatre were cleaned and redecorated, paid for by Theatrical Entertainments and at the next annual meeting the committee is once more stressing the Educational Role of the Hospital re its affiliation to the *Birmingham Medical School, students being able to attend to receive Clinical instruction. *Founded in 1834 by William Sands Cox, a surgeon at the Birmingham Dispensary. In 1843 it became the Queen's College.

A change in Privilege's for Governors, is announced; "... for each £1-1-0 Annual Subscription, 2 inpatients tickets available for 14 days or 6 outpatient for 6 weeks, each entitle patient to medicine and attendance. Donation of £21 makes a Life governor, also Ministers of Religion preaching on our behalf, both entitled £1-1-0 privileges in respect of every £10-10s. One ticket entitles a Single Truss; 2 Double Truss; 4 Small Scarpa; 6 Large Scarpa; 6 Simple Leg-irons; 12 Double Leg-irons; 12 Simple spinal; 15 Compound spinal ..."

During the year 1893 the deaths of two past Presidents are announced; Lord Calthorpe and Lord Dartmouth. and W. Suckley enters as a Hon. Cons. Surgeon. A move towards an Appeal for a Convalescent Cottage Fund arises when Captain and Mrs. Grice Hutchinson, due to absence from home, handed over their Longden cottage to the Hospital. 27 children were entertained there under a Hospital Nurse, however it was felt that a Country Home (closer to Birmingham) would be beneficial. The need for a trained Masseuse was first raised.

The fear of the Workhouse as being "... the only alternative ..." for 'chronic patients' requiring lengthy periods in Hospital, was clearly another reason for seeking additional 'after care' premises. The secure status of the current hospital is assured when the Committee states "... a new lease, for 7 years from 25th March 1895." Two more deaths are announced. Mr. Edward Freer and Mr. W. Crompton (after 17 years as Consulting Surgeon).

Miss Wolseley was appointed Dispenser in 1896. and Miss Glenville, Matron 1897 (replacing Miss Burgess, 7 years in the post). With a Liability of £1,514-4s-4d to the Bank, another warning,

"... with this large overdraft it will be absolutely necessary to close some of the wards unless immediate substantial assistance is received". The Convalescent Home fund is proceeding 'very slowly'. The Hospital Medical Staff first record their appreciation, of the 'new photography' in the more exact diagnosis of obscure deformities.

Further 'X-ray' developments appear over the following year, with Mr. Hall-Edwards continuing to give the Hospital the benefit of his great ability

1897

The Matron and Nurses were found to bring a ittle sunshine into the lives of their unfortunate patients

copyright: Birmingham Post & Mail

Mr Edward Ansell
President Royal Orthopaedic & Spinal Hospital
ROH. Reports 1922 - 24 Photo: Brian Jones

and experience in the application of X-rays. An important addition to the usefulness of the hospital was the setting-up of a separate room for carrying out Massage, Electrical and Medico-Kinetic work. Dr. Charles Warden's resignation is announced in 1899, his replacement being Mr. W. Edward Bennett.

Outpatients had been removed to a separate building No. 22 Great Charles Street, taken during the year, in order to improve sanitary conditions for inpatients. The Anaesthetist Dr. Grinling resigned, through ill health. The start of the 20th Century found the hospital with a Matron/Dispenser, Miss Graves; and with a financial deficiency of £732-6s-71/2d; it is not surprising to read "... A New Hospital is most desirable ..." as the "... Hospital Resources are full to capacity; Attendances 10,180; New Cases 1,587; Operations 806; inpatients 735; country patients 396; a small and inconvenient overcrowded outpatient department. ...".

Dr. W. Duncan Lawrie was temporally appointed Assistant Surgeon during the absence of Mr. E.L.Freer who had volunteered for Military Duty in South Africa. (Presumably the Boer War). The death of Queen Victoria, 22nd January 1901 naturally marked a sad day for the Orthopaedic Hospital, "... the Hospital has lost its most influential Patron ... a fund is opened for the purpose of dedicating 3 beds to Her Memory and, the hope, that the appeal will not only provide a fitting memorial, but a large increase in the Funds of the Charity ...". Some 18 months on 'inadequate support' is again declared. "The present premises are yearly becoming more unsuitable ... to carry on the increased work which is accruing from year to year, and unless a very considerable increase is forthcoming, work will have to be materially curtailed and 'Any scheme for building a New Hospital must be Indefinitely postponed'.

Mr. E. Luke Freer "... having served throughout the South Africa War, resigned his post of Assistant Surgeon". Mr. Lawrie filling the vacancy. St. Thomas's Hospital and Children's Hospital, Great Ormond Street, London, now played its part by providing the next Matron, Miss Margaret Nicoll, who was to replace Miss Glanville, after 6 years in the post. During the year 1902/3 a scheme had been inaugurated for the 'Instruction of Nursing Staff by means of Lectures in Elementary Anatomy, Physiology and General

Nursing knowledge.

A Scarlet Fever outbreak in early 1902 resulted in no new cases being admitted until the Hospital was free from infection; no surgical operations and the isolation of the outbreak Ward. Miss Clarke was appointed as Dispenser, and the June Celebrations for the Coronation of Edward V11 and Queen Alexandra, resulted in a dinner being given to the children, and supper to the adult patients. The Nursing Staff, in addition to a dinner, were each to be allowed leave for one day and one night. Most Loyally, Mr Edward Bennett, Honorary Surgeon, provided the Hospital with a Flag. .

In April 1903 the Medical Committee appointed a new Dispenser, Miss Lydia Little of Selly Hill, Birmingham, and the following month that committee reports on the 'Treatment of Congenital Dislocation of the Hip'. - by Apparatus; by Operative reduction; and, by Forcible reduction, going into detail of the pros and cons, and enquiring as to the results, suffering of patients and the care of the 'cases treated in this hospital'.

Priorities at September 1903 were, the Committee having ordered 6 new chimney-pots to replace the damaged ones; authorised spending a sum not exceeding £10 in furnishing Matron's room, and appointing as Deputy Matron, Mrs. Frost. Miss Nicoll, the Matron was authorised to purchase slippers for the use of the patients.

The year 1904 saw further moves towards a new hospital site. Three schemes being put forward by the Building and Sites Committee:-

1. To acquire freehold land at the corner of Easy Row/Edmund Street. The objection to this being that it was an impossible site to place lavatories and other sanitary conveniences, in direct communication with each ward. (!).

2. To acquire a piece of land in the Crescent, next to that already occupied by the Crescent Nurses Home. Senior Hon. Surgeon objected to the situation.

3. To retain the present site on which the Hospital stands. Agreed to proceed as there were several advantages, viz; No change of address; Being situated at the corner of two roads, there would be considerable air-space, and, the whole of the buildings required for outpatient and inpatient departments could be placed on site without undue crowding.

A slight diversion is worthy of mention, with the Committee Chairman reporting that '... it had been noted that Operations were going on until 4 o'clock in the afternoon'. The circumstance was explained by an Hon. Surgeon, and it was resolved that 'the surgeons be requested to commence operations by 9 o'clock'.

Augustus Clay resigns his position as Hon. Surgeon in 1904, being appointed Consulting Surgeon, and is replaced by Mr. Frank Barnes. The condition of the existing demands of the outpatient department of the Hospital, and justification for its needs, pleads that "... it requires more accommodation than would generally be supposed; as all instruments have to be carefully fitted to patients and considerable space wanted for daily massage and gymnastic exercises"

The Committee having been concerned at a complaint that had been made by the Public, in a newspaper earlier in the year, responded by saying "... your Committee are most anxious to provide new and suitable buildings, but rely entirely upon your generosity..."

Good News from the Sunday Hospital Fund, was being considered in May 1904. when at the Annual meeting of the friends and supporters of the Fund, a Resolution was passed in favour of dividing the Collection Annually amongst the Hospitals and Charities, with the hope that interest in, and the amount of the Collection would be increased if it were divided annually, in the same proportions as at present, 1/3 to the General Hospital, 1/3 to the Queen's Hospital, and 1/3 to the Amalgamated Charities.

Now a complaint from within the hospital. "The action of the Chairman in opposing the running of a Service of Electric Trams along Newhall Street and Great Charles Street, was approved".

The appointment of Messrs. Thorneywork as instrument makers has previously been stated, the following letter continues the story. On the 11th October 1904 is received a quotation:- " As requested, I have pleasure in sending you a list of the price of Surgical Instruments, and at the same time I should like to mention that owing to the death of Mr. Thorneywork, Mr. J.S.Thorneywork has also withdrawn from the business, and in consequence the writer is carrying on the business himself. I may say I have been connected with the above firm since a lad of 14 yrs old. I have well considered the prices ... I have reduced most of the Surgical

Instruments, viz., Leg-Irons 3/6, Hip Inst's. 3/6, Knee Inst.s 3/6, Spinal Vests 3/6, Spinal Inst.s 6/-, Large French Crutches 3/6, Scarpa Shoes 1/6 etc., Trusting that this will meet with your approval, and assuring you that I will always do my best to give every satisfaction. I am charging the Instruments had in August at the revised list.

Yours respectfully.

H. Strong.

A suite of rooms for nurses had been taken in Cornwall Buildings, and fixtures purchased at the cost of £13-10-0. In March, 1905 we hear that 'The children's Ward is to be refitted and 'that a window or large ventilator is to be placed in the operating theatre near the apex of the roof.'. Complaints about the 'operating table' having been made, resulted in the need for a new one. Could these last two events have brought about a subsequent complaint from an adjacent company, in Great Charles Street re - 'the unacceptable noise on operating days'?

The condition of the temporary outpatient premises in Great Charles Street is still a source of anxiety. However the Hospital is given notice to quit the building by the Corporation, the site to be used for the Council House Extension.. A £20,000 Appeal was considered, for the building of a completely new hospital, this was dropped in deference to the request from the Queen's Hospital who were also making an appeal. The Trustees of the Colmore Estate had offered generous terms for the erection of a New Hospital but it was decided first to erect an Outpatient Department, (at a cost of some £4,000) on land adjoining the Newhall Street hospital. but still in Great Charles Street. The Foundation Stone was laid, by the Lord Mayor of Birmingham (Councillor A.J.Reynolds), on the 2nd April 1906.

The death of Walter Carless Freer is announced in 1906, after 23 years as Senior Consulting Surgeon, and the committee acknowledges receipt of Legacies from; the Late Richard Cadbury (brother of George), £2,500; the Late Joseph Gillott £500 and, the Late Edward Ansell £100. Mr. Duncan Lawrie resigns his post to take up private practice in Llandudno, and the Hospital was ordering its coal, 'by the boat-load' for the coming Winter.(Well, it was near to the Canal).

Reports at the next Annual Meeting express the need to step up

Winter.(Well, it was near to the Canal).

Reports at the next Annual Meeting express the need to step up canvassing for subscriptions in the districts around Birmingham as once more, many cases received for treatment, are not contributing a like proportion to the hospital's support. The General Committee is being recommended, the following year, to procure estimates for the installation and maintenance of complete equipment for taking Radiography at the Hospital.

Following a report from Mr. Frank Barnes, October 3rd. 1907, the outpatient department was to be closed on Saturday mornings due to lack of support.

1908 records, that after 25 years as Honorary Surgeon, Mr. William Thomas was appointed Hon. Consulting Surgeon, his post being filled by Mr. F. Victor Milward. After 4 years Miss Nicol has resigned as Matron, the committee recommending the appointment of Miss Mildred Moore as the new Matron. Sympathy is called for Dr. Hall-Edwards - Radiographer, in his illness, whose importance is not just within the city but throughout the country. Mr. W.A.Cadbury (a son of Richard Cadbury) makes a gift of a Tennis Court and Recreation Ground for the use of Nurses of the smaller hospitals of the city.

An outbreak of Diphtheria in the hospital was reported having occurred in 1909, resulting in closure for some weeks. The resulting costs of £900 for the necessary sanitary improvements, of which only £228-9-0 was recouped, from a private appeal, again raised the call -

"... The available funds of the Hospital will not allow it to be carried on unless some marked improvement is forthcoming.". Following the death on May 6th 1910, of Edward V11, the following resolution was, proposed, seconded and passed in silence:-

"That the Committee of this Hospital respectfully offer their expression of profound sympathy, to her Majesty Queen Alexandra, to their Majesties the King and Queen, and the Members of the Royal Family, in the irreparable loss they have sustained by the lamented death of the beloved King".

The General Committee at its July 20th meeting records:-

"That the following letter be framed and hung up in the Board Room to match those already up". Note the signatory.

Home Office, Whitehall, 21st June 1910

My Lord Marquess,

I am commanded by the King to convey to your Lordship hereby His Majesty's Thanks for the Loyal and Dutiful Resolution of the Committee of the Royal Orthopaedic and Spinal Hospital, on the occasion of the lamented death of His Late Majesty King Edward the Seventh. I am to say that the expression of sympathy with Queen Alexandra has been laid before Her Majesty, who desires me to communicate to you Her Thanks.

I am My Lord Marquess.   Your Lordship's Obedient Servant

Winston S. Churchill.

Also in 1910, there is reference to the Cripples Union -

"... correspondence with the Crippled Children's Union as to the non-supply of tickets in accordance with the guarantees issued by the Union." (there was some confusion regarding the ticket system, going back a number of years. It was amicably resolved.). The Birmingham Mail Christmas Tree Fund, is continuing its support for hospitals. In April 1911, the Editor having again made a grant, from the fund, to the *Northfield Home, and that this Hospital (Royal Orthopaedic) should be given similar facilities for sending outpatients as were arranged last year. *this must be the Woodlands, and the 'facilities' mentioned would refer to an allocation of beds agreed with the Cripple's Union.

Miss Roberts was appointed Masseuse as from September - 11th, 1911, she being put in charge of the Exercises as well as Massage and to delegate work to an Assistant. Coal is being supplied at 13/6 per ton.

The health of Matron, Miss Moore was not good resulting in frequent absences, her stand-in being Sister Tucker. The Massage Sub-committee however records, in December 1911 a scheme produced by Miss Moore setting out proposals for the training of nurses. Stating the arrangements at the Royal National Orthopaedic Hospital, London, for an 18 month course for Staff Nurses. The nurses paying 6 guineas for instruction, 3 hours a day learning and practicing Massage and ward duties, and £1-11-6 Examination Fee. Matron advises an increase to two Staff Nurses each being trained by Miss Roberts for the Incorporated Society of Trained Masseuse Examinations. Each to pay 4 guineas to the Hospital, and £1-11-6 Examination Fee. The Ward maid is, however, to give up her bedroom to the Nurse, and sleep out at the cost of £5 pa.

March 1912, finds further improvements in communication, with the procuring of a portable switchboard for the use of the surgeons, and the death of the Most Noble the Marquess of Hertford, is announced, who had been President for 28 years. A somewhat unusual 'future' legacy is declared, in a letter dated April 28th 1912 received by the Trustees, from 'Truly yours Sarah Ball'.

" Sirs, I have to inform you of the death of my sister, Mrs. Maria Cole, so that now my life is the only one between your full possession of the £2,000, for you to get on my demise, I so gladly arranged.

My present address is 931 East 35 Street, Brooklyn, N.Y. USA"

The resignation of Mr. Woodward, Honorary Surgeon is announced in 1912, and the Most Honourable the Marquess of Northampton takes on the Presidency at the November meeting, at which the death of Dr. Charles Warden, a member of the Honorary Staff since 1853, was announced, (Having been an Honorary Surgeon for 43 of these years, Dr. Warden's longevity of service is, I believe, unique in this hospital history. He ranks with the name Freer, the family whose members served for 87 years as surgeons to the Institution, continually, from its conception in 1817). Mr. Percival Mills joins the Honorary surgeons, at the end of this year.

At the beginning of 1913, Miss Moore's letter of resignation is received, and from 54 sets of Testimonials applying for the post of Matron, 6 were short listed from which Miss Hadley was appointed. Miss Hadley, who was from the General Hospital, was due to commence her duties on the 5th April, but was allowed to take a holiday before doing so. Mr. Tattersell, the hospital Porter, was granted a 2/- per week increase in his salary, effective from the date of his forthcoming marriage. Following the death of the President, the Marquess of Northampton, Mr. Edward Ansell was invited to take the post. (a most fitting honour in view of his invaluable contribution, particularly with the Crippled children of the city).

The year ends with, Mr. C. J. Thompson being appointed Clinical

Assistant and Sister Gray, who had become Resident Masseuse and Assistant Matron, 3 months earlier, resigned as she had been appointed Lady Superintendent of a Private Nursing Home in Sussex. The Finance Committee recommended a reduction in the number of beds in September 1914, due to the state of the accounts as at the year ending 30th June, and the first World war was to claim its first hospital recruit, when Dr. Thompson resigns having volunteered for Military Duties, in December 1914.

9th February 1915, notes an investigation into the 'cost of telephone installation between the inpatient and outpatient departments, and at the next Annual Report the hospital takes a leaf from the Cripple's Union, when it commences case histories of patients, in its literature, one such being:- Edward _?_ aged 47, came here as a last resource, though he was not given any hope of being a successful case. He was quite unable to do his work as he could not stoop, his left hip having become quite stiff. On June 7th 1915 an operation was performed. In five weeks he was walking about and is now back at work again, delighted with himself.

All three Honorary Surgeons are engaged on War-service , and the late Massage Sister had left to act a Assistant Matron at Highbury, while her successor has also to take up Military work. May 1916 finds Matron appointing Miss King and Miss Darby (afternoon only), as Assistant Masseuse. A committee member Mr. George Bryson, hears of the death of his son, Captain Landor Bryson on the battlefield in France.

At the 99th Annual Report, Miss Smith, (Fanny Smith) is appointed Assistant Matron. War casualties now appear in the case- studies. Private Samuel _?_ , after treatment in a Military Hospital was discharged as unfit. He was admitted to this Hospital July 23rd, 1916, and ordered Massage and Electrical treatment. A plaster cast was applied and he was discharged on August 30th much improved.

At the General Committee of December 1916, the running of the hospital under war-time conditions is stated; the hospital keeping six beds at the general disposal of the Local Statutory Committee for male patients requiring orthopaedic treatment, and, the committee desires to do all in their power to meet the need of Soldiers for special orthopaedic treatment, by placing 14 beds at the disposal of the Military Authorities.

Miss Verney was appointed as non-resident Masseuse in June 1917. The approaching Centenary, is of course, clouded by the war, however it was intended that the Lord Mayor be contacted with a view to the City authorising a Flag day. Another death is announced, when Mr. J.E.Pritchard, (also a Committee member), learned of the loss of his only son , in France, from wounds received in action.

The 100th Annual Report held on October 9th 1917 adds information as to the need to maintain the ordinary life of the Hospital. One of the smaller wards being enlarged; 11 additional beds equipped; necessary sanitary alterations, all of which amounted to £254. an expense partly met by two donations amounting to £150. With £104 balance, the committee was looking for further donations.

Discharged Soldiers were another special feature of the year. Up to the end of June 1917, 16 men had been treated as inpatients, and 70 had attended the outpatient department. The Massage and Electrical Departments were opened all day, instead of afternoons only, requiring a considerable increase in Masseuse. Major Bennett was commended for having devoted so much of his time to the work of the Hospital. Mr. Barnes and Mr. Mills being still absent on Military Duties. Mr. Leather, Resident Surgical Officer of the General Hospital had carried on for Mr. Mills, and Dr. Allan, a Clinical Assistant was of great assistance.

As the centenary year drew to a close it is recorded that a Report had been received from the Ministry of Pensions, stating that it was intended that an Orthopaedic Sub-centre may be set up in Birmingham. It was suggested that this Hospital might possibly take over the old Children's Hospital (Steel House Lane or Broad Street ?), and move the Inpatient Department there and the whole of these premises (Newhall Street ?), might be used for Outpatient work.

The first 'post 1st world war' Annual Report expands on the treatment of discharged soldiers. 291 of the 2,811 patients, that had presented themselves at the Hospital. The first eight months of the year the Military Ward beds had been occupied by men from the 1st Southern General Hospital, these beds subsequently being taken over by the Ministry of

Pensions. The Austin Motor Company had assisted in the urgent needs of the outpatient department by their donation towards the cost of additional electrical equipment. The Matron, Miss Hadley was heartily congratulated, by the General Committee, in connection with the Military work of the Hospital.

The Medical Committee having successfully coped, (throughout the war),having had the great assistance of Mr. Leather, Dr. Allan, also the occasional help of Dr. Peel, Dr. Coole Neale, Dr. Ainscoe and Lieut. Ainscoe, with Dr. Jordan, the sheet anchor, as Anaesthetist and Physician. Appreciation was also expressed to the Committee of Moseley Hall, for placing beds at 'our disposal', and to the Cripple's Union for supplying spinal carriages and 'taking many tubercular cases into the Woodlands'.

The report for 1919-20, regrets the long waiting lists, "... The Hospital has been worked to its utmost capacity ..." and we learn that 101, Newhall Street, lately used as a Servants' Training Home', had been, temporarily, taken for a Nurses Home. A generous, anonymous friend had given £590 5s 8d, so paying off the 1917-18 deficiency. It is stated also that with regard to the re-building of the hospital , "... the work of the inpatient department would be carried out with much greater success in one of the suburbs instead of the city centre. With this object in view, land has been secured at Quinton...".

During the year, Dr. Wilson has been appointed Assistant Anaesthetist, Mr. J. B. Leather's appointment confirmed and Mr. Naughton Dunn Hon. Surgeon. Miss West has been giving weekly lectures of 11/2 hours duration in the Theory and Practice of Massage. (Miss West was, later, to give lectures to pupils "... of our Massage School...", at the General Hospital). The Massage staff being:- Miss Jameson, Head Masseuse; Sister Shaw a Trained Nurse; Miss Bariorll; Miss Hulley; Miss Perkins and Miss L. McKenzie. (July 1920 saw the appointment of Miss Barwell as Head Masseuse with Miss Tolefree, Assistant).

Discussions on the co-ordination of the work of the various voluntary hospitals, and after-care, particularly with relation to prolonged diseases. have been approved. "...Unnecessary work being caused by patients changing from one Institution to another when only partly cured...".

1920-21 negotiations were in progress with the Cripples Union, for closer co-operation, and, the Committee acknowledges two donations, wiping off the 1918-19 debts, also the cheque for £550 from Messrs. Ansell's Brewery, "through our President, Mr. Edward Ansell".

The Committee was pleased to receive the following information, from the Blue Coat School, (then sited in St. Philip's Place), "... that one of their old boys had made a fortune in Australia and wanted to help Birmingham Charities". The distribution of the ticket system took a turn, when in June 1920 it was announced "that four tickets be issued for each guinea subscribed, instead of six".

The Finance Committee were concerned, the following month, at the costs of aftercare for Tubercular Cases in Birmingham. Resolving that "... where patients have to be visited in their homes, the charge shall be 15/- per head, per week, and 2/6 for those able to attend the outpatients department. Charges to include all ordinary dressings and bandages". They also appointed an Almoner, Miss Mountford.

A most generous bequest of £22,000 (from the late John Avins), enabled the hospital to press ahead with a workshop for the manufacture of Surgical Instruments, £2,000 of which being for that purpose. The other £20,000 going towards the extension of the Hospital.

The Annual Report given on 30th May, 1924, refers to an opportunit, 'only just arisen', to acquire premises suitable for the extension of the work of the Hospital. (this move must have been triggered by the breakdown of negotiations with the Cripples Union). The Committee was seeking co-operation with any institution doing similar work, and it was thought that, following meetings with the General Hospital, a big scheme might develop over the next two or three years, enabling one big Outpatient Clinic, where all Orthopaedic cases could be treated. The Medical Report for the year ending 31st December 1923, announces two new appointments; Dr.T.L.Hardy as Physician to the Hospital, the need being justified thus "... Many patients with disease of the nervous system suffer from deformity, as this is frequently to them the most obvious sign of disease, they attend the Orthopaedic Hospital". Mr. Wilson Stuart joining as Assistant Surgeon in November, this being a revival of an old appointment, made necessary by the pressure of work in the outpatient department.

The end of 1924, finds the negotiations, not just back on track, but, reaching a successful conclusion. "During the latter part of the year the Committee of this Hospital met in consultation with the Committee of the Birmingham Cripples Union, and, after very careful consideration, a scheme was formulated for the Amalgamation. This therefore will be the last Report of the Royal Orthopaedic and Spinal Hospital as a separate Institution".

Two additional points of interest are stated firstly the announcement that as the outpatient department has grown so rapidly, further accommodation is urgently required "... your Committee consider themselves very fortunate in being able to secure the Broad Street premises. (the old Children's Hospital). A house situated at 22 Vicarage Road, Edgbaston, had also been made available (through Mr. J. H. Francis, Committee Chairman). as an additional inpatient department., with accommodation for about 30 patients, following structural alterations and erection of verandahs.

Chapter 2 deals more fully with the Amalgamation details, as seen by the Cripples Union negotiators. I close this chapter however by referring to a statement, given by the Union's chief negotiator Mr. H.F.Harvey, in 1948, at a Commemorative Dinner, following the (next upheaval) 'Parting of the Ways' and the N.H.S., which, in retrospect, places the protracted negotiations in true perspective.

"The amalgamation negotiations with the Royal Orthopaedic Hospital did not go smoothly at first. All that the Joint-Committee seemed to be able to agree about was that amalgamation was desirable. After one breakdown, he and (the late) J.H.Francis met at a dinner and decided to ask Sir Gilbert Barling to act as Independent Chairman of the Joint-Committee. He remembered saying to Sir Gilbert 'If we don't agree, just knock our heads together'. That proved to be unnecessary for from then on everything was plain sailing and from the first days of the honeymoon it proved a happy marriage. It inaugurated an era of progress which converted Woodlands from a small Children's Hospital with less than a hundred beds into one of the leading Orthopaedic Hospitals in the country".

Chapter 2

The Crippled Children's Union
1896 - 1925

*Can I see another's Woe,
and not be in sorrow too?
Can I see another's grief,
And not seek for kind relief.

The Birmingham and District Crippled Children's Union was founded as
'but a small department' of the Hurst Street Mission, (opposite to today's
Birmingham Hippodrome on the corner of Inge Street) in 1896. This
Mission, dating back to 1846, had been renamed the 'People's Hall' in 1886.
Mr. W. J. Clarke was the Honorary Secretary, being the Missionary. Other
functions of the Mission were; Police-Aided Association for Clothing
Destitute Children; Distressed Military Veteran's Association, and, Court
and Alley Open-Air Concerts Association. In connection, with the last of
these, the then known 80 crippled children in the town, were invited to
parties.

A meeting was held on March 23rd, 1899, (at the People's Hall) at which
Mr. Clarke states "... The work has grown very rapidly, so much so that
nearly the whole of the time of my Assistant Mr. F. Mathews, has lately
been given to it. This still increasing development and the knowledge thus
gained of the many ways in which these afflicted children need not only
kindly sympathy but practical help, seem to indicate that the time has
arrived when the work and the further development of which the Union is
capable should be taken in hand by an independent Association".

The subsequent public meeting outlined the aims; 'To promote the
interests of all Birmingham Crippled Children of School age by; Supplying
Medical and Surgical advice that parents are unable to procure; Education
for those unable to attend school. (and ensure it for those that could).;
Brighten their lives by parties, entertainments etc.; Arrange for sick
children to go to Convalescent Homes, and -

*Quotation from the First Annual Report, 1901.
is taken from 'Sons of Innocence' by William Blake, dated 1789.

45

- Summer Holidays; Teach Trades and occupations. On September 29th, 1899, the Secretary's report announces that an Annual Gathering had been held at the Botanical Gardens (in July) raising £32-9-1d. (such events had clearly been going on for some years), The Unions obtaining of 'Notes' from the Royal Orthopaedic and Spinal Hospital is another form of income. "... we sent out circulars to 664 subscribers, the effort involving an expenditure of £1-10-2d ... receiving in response thereto 173 notes which bought in the ordinary way would have cost £30-5-6d; a clear nett gain to the Union of £28-15-4d. (this system must have been that referred to, in 1910, by the Orthopaedic Hospital).

Mr. Mathews is shortly to take on his prominent role, when with the termination of his position as Assistant Missionary, he having played a very important part in the practical work in connection with the Union, he was appointed Visiting Superintendent of the C.C.U. (at a salary of £59 pa. (for the first sixth months), and on the retirement of Mr. Clarke, Frank Mathews was elected Secretary, (for the time being - and was to stay 21 years).

The Officers and Committee for 1900-1901 were;

President; The Right Hon. The Lord Mayor

Vice-Presidents; The Countess of Warwick; The Lord Bishop of Coventry; The Right Hon. Joseph Chamberlain, M.P.

The Right Hon. Jesse Collins, M.P. J.T.Middlemore.

Ebenezer Parkes. M.P. Sir John Holder, Bart. George Cadbury.

Rev. J.G.Emanuel. Rev. J.H.Jowett, M.A.

Hon. Treasurer, Mrs. H.P.Gibson. Hon. Sec. Rev. A.A.Charlesworth.

Secretary; Mr. Frank Mathews, People's Hall, Hurst Street'

The General Committee, under the Chairmanship of W.H.Ryland being:-

Mrs. Belfield; Miss E. Jones; Mr. E.Ansell; Mrs. Freeman,

Miss I.King; Miss E.Belfield; Mrs. Gibbs; Miss Litchfield,

Mr.H.Bisseker; Mrs. H.P.Gibson; Miss Lloyd; Mr. G.F.Goodman,

Mrs.W.H.Ryland; Miss Staveley; Mr.W.Gibbs; Mrs. E.Wheeler,

Miss G.Whitmore; Miss K.Whitmore; Mr. Holden; Miss Barnett,

Mr. M.Hooper; Miss Cale; Rev. A.A.Charlesworth; Mr. G.Jackson;

Miss Deakin; Rev. N.M.Hennesy; Mr. W.J.Nichols; Miss E.Jones,

Rev. L.P.Jacks; Mr. J.Stych.

Honorary Surgeons; E.Luke Freer; Jordon Lloyd and William Thomas.

(The presence of Mr. A Holden, in committee, brings to light another reason for Frank Mathew's work with the Mission. Mr Holden, a Birmingham Councillor, ran a 'Paint and Varnish' business in Bradford Street. The Holden family all attended the Hurst Street Mission, and he regularly organised parties at his cottage garden, near Knowle. One of his daughters was Edith Holden, [later to write 'The Diary of an Edwardian Lady], and Frank Mathews courted her sister Evelyn, marrying in 1904.)

In the Second Annual Report,(Offices now at 46 Newhall Hill) 'Six Headings' are stated, under which the Union's work is being carried on:-

(1) Visitation, enabling accurate knowledge of not only the crippled children, but also the parents and family conditions. Parental responsibility is stressed, and that they should contribute money. If so poor, they are, in the case of surgical boots, asked to pay in small amounts, toward repairs. Parents are advised of the 'unwisdom' of changing hospitals, failure to keep appointments, and failing to carry out doctor's orders. (2) Hospital, During the first year 212 cases have been treated in Hospitals and Medical Charities. (3) Convalescent, 123 cases have been sent away to homes. The pressure on the Convalescent Homes, at that time, is placed in perspective, with the statement that there are only some 80 beds for all the convalescent children in Birmingham and the District within 25 miles. (this includes; Moseley Hall; Solihull; Leamington; Warwick; Stratford-on-Avon; Blackwell; Hampton-in-Arden; Rugby; Sutton Coldfield).

Frank Mathews announces, "...that we have taken the bold step of starting a Convalescent Home of our own". The Committee granted £50, having taken the Cottage at Chadwick End, near Knowle. (which it was to use over the following 10 years). It had accommodation for 10 children and a Matron (Miss Redman) and Assistant Matron had been appointed. (Detail of the home and its lands deserve further comment, which will be found later in this history).

(4) Education, "The importance of education to cripples cannot be over-estimated", says Frank Mathews, " it gives an interest to otherwise

hopelessly dreary lives". He continues by hoping that the Birmingham Board will enable the forming of special classes, so opening the way to a regular and systematic education, to those for which it was at present denied. The holding of classes, "of our own", for; Basket Making; Reading and Writing; Drawing; Shorthand; Candle-shades and Fly-rest work, were in progress, which were also being carried out for teaching in the homes. Type-writing was to be added later, so enabling advanced pupils to take up positions as Clerks. This leads naturally to heading No. (5) Industrial , A visit to London had found that a most successful industry for crippled boys, that paid well, was Relief-Stamping and Copper-Plating. After a 3 year apprenticeship, a lad could earn 15/- rising to 35/-, also the trade was most suitable for cured spinal cases.

(6) Parties, Being the ground-base, of the Union's early efforts, and with Mr. E. Ansell a founder member of the committee, the "... sunshine is put into the lives of our cripples...". His kindness in bearing the total cost of the Town Hall party, for the third year in succession, was acknowledged. (this was to continue for many years ahead.).

These were not just ideals, but rules for a way of life driven through the energies of Frank Mathews. There were by now some 398 children's names on the Register. The 'Visiting' required the obtaining, training and organising of ladies. However Frank himself visited every child, every home, not just once, but at least three times each year. (Later testimony will tell of his great love for children). Such was his devotion that within two years, his efforts were being described, in an article published in 'Women's Workers', written by Mrs. Nolan-Slaney, a Health Visitor, by permission of the Health Committee of the City of Birmingham, thus:-

"That Christ-like charity, the Crippled Children's Union, is another organisation which pierces through the social scale till it reaches the submerged."

No greater compliment could have marked the founding of that Union, and the vision and determination in particular of Mr. Frank Mathews, at such an early stage of its development.

It is important I feel to take but one-example of the work. Each Annual Report would give examples of "... Cases for which we Appeal for Special help" ; One such being:- " ... that of a boy referred to us by the Aston Relief Association, was paralysed in one hand and badly in one leg. It was suggested to us that it would be well to get him into a Home for Incurables. The circumstances were very sad. His mother was dead. His father was out of work and his health had broken down, in looking for it. They were homeless, and father and son slept in wash-houses or wherever they could, till the boy went in to the Infirmary. It was there that he was seen by Mr. Mathews, whose experience suggested that the paralysis in the hand at any rate was of so slight a character that good feeding and a little drill would clear it.

As the child was only five, and on the principal that home influences are an essential element of moral development it was thought best to board him with foster-parents. He is now with another child living very happy at Rowington. The hand is quite right and the leg is getting stronger every month."

The Union has succeeded in obtaining school places, and setting up special schools, Dean Street, (near the Bull-Ring) had 43 children in attendance the statement "... that inspite of their disabilities, these children suffer, there is no happier school in the city...", speaks for itself. 1903 sees a move towards help for adult cripples. "... We welcome the advent to Birmingham of the 'Guild of Brave Poor Things' a Society, successful in other towns and London, that has done splendid service. ...". They cater for cripples over 14 years of age, the Union had handed to them 34 cases.

The Union has dealt with 1,066 children during 1905, 800 names being on the Register. Clearly the indoor accommodation for 10 children, at Chadwick End has been stretched, as we hear "... The large tent in use at our convalescent cottage, for six months last year has again been erected this summer, enabling us to take a much larger number, for longer periods". Even at this early stage, demand is becoming greater than space will allow, and the call goes out "... The convalescent work of the Union, however, cannot be considered as satisfactory until we get a properly equipped Convalescent and Nursing Home."

Plans for a Grandiose Convalescent Home, were drawn up by

C.E.Bateman, F.R.B.A. Architect, close to the Chadwick End Cottage, sited on the corner of Oldwych Lane and Chadwick Lane,

During the following year, an appeal is made for £6,000, of which all but £2,600 had been received or promised.The Chadwick End home, now having Nurse Worrell as Matron, and Miss Mole, Assistant Matron; had taken 150 children, who had played in the Marquee; or wandered through the fields and lanes. A sand-garden had been donated, it being stated "... the donors would have felt amply repaid in seeing 'Baby Ben' making his sand-pies, or little 'helpless Annie' lying there contentedly all day, building her sand castles".

Referring to the employment needs of the cripples, good news is received, with a member of the Jeweller's Association who had already employed six lads, preferring them, as he said, to ordinary boy's "as they stick to their work better". A Weaving School had been set up at 320 Summer Lane , at which 8 girls were attending, and Miss Thomas is the 'Visiting Teacher' for 'Home' work, this being for children totally unfit for ordinary employment.

The eighth Annual Report notes ' the kindness of members of the Midlands Motor Union in giving 120 children the pleasure of a motor-ride to Castle Bromwich'. One little girl remarking afterwards "I'm glad I'm a poor cripple, or I shouldn't never have been to the motor-party". And the report for 1907-08 records the move of the Weaving School to 160 Broad Street. (Not the later Orthopaedic Clinic site) having now been placed in the hands of a Special Committee, but still as part of the Union. The principal event of the year was of course "the *magnificent gift of the Woodlands by Mr. George Cadbury, for the purpose of a Nursing and Convalescent Home."(Offer acknowledged in letter dated 22nd November 1907 from Crippled Children's Union, to George Cadbury)

The Union's Secretary, Frank Mathews. states the philosophy of the Union to events, (noting, of course, that he is not a medical man) in his subsequent comment re this gift, adding " ... Mr. Cadbury has generously added to his gift, by entirely re-arranging the garden-grounds so as to make

Chadwick End. Cripples Union Sanatorium Home, Oldwych Lane
source: Roy Calfield

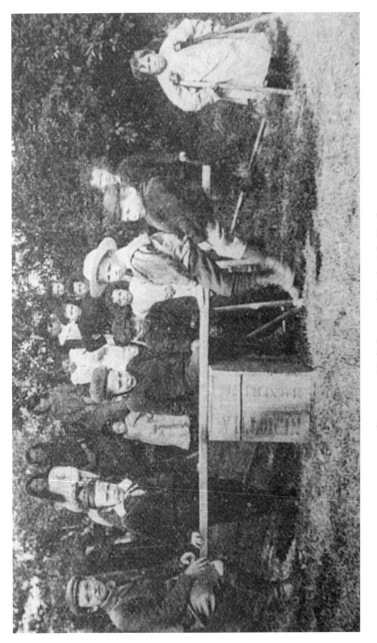

Summer Holiday at Chadwick End
Source: Crippled Children's Annual Union reports. 1900-1908
photo: Brian Jones

them an ideal playground for children. It is difficult for anyone not intimately concerned in convalescent work to realise the value of such a gift ... It is essential in cases of hip disease indeed in all tubercular bone disease to transfer the patient immediately on the commencement of the disease to a place where absolute rest can be insisted upon. Where this can be done deformity can be reduced to a minimum, and the children are more speedily and effectually cured".

A description of the Woodlands,(House and lands) at the time of George Cadbury's purchase in 1899, and a view as to why he subsequently gave it to the Crippled Chuildren's Union, is given in Chapter 5.

As a result of this gift the Union will now be able to withdraw all children at present in Convalescent Homes. The *Chadwick End home is then referred to thus:- "... the tent that we used was very worn last year and has been completely wrecked by autumn gales. In view of the opening of the new home next autumn (anticipated) it is not advisable to purchase a new one ...". This loss meant that they had no-where to send "... our three to six week cases ...", this problem was alleviated when the Hospital Saturday Committee took 23 children, free of charge, into their Great Barr house.

The first steps leading to an amalgamation with the Adult Cripple's Guild were taken with the uniting of the industrial work of the two Societies.

Discussions had taken place, even before the opening of the Woodlands (1909), with the Royal Orthopaedic and Spinal Hospital, with regard to "... some terms being arranged under which convalescent patients would be received at the Woodlands from them. ... the Committee recognising notes up to a limit of 150, for each period of six months, and, in the matter of Daily Mail beds offering to keep two beds, at the disposal of the Hospital ... that children should not be over 14 years of age."

The 11th Annual Report (1911), of the Cripple's Union, (held at 45 Cornwall Buildings), referring to the opening in May 1909, adds that George Cadbury also paid for the whole of the costs of alterations, (with special wards for open-air treatment). Only part of the house being occupied, 58 children having been there during the year, 37 beds now occupied 30 by Birmingham cases others paid for by the Selly Oak (6) and

Smethwick (1), Branches. The Honorary Medical Officer was Dr. Guy Dain, and Matron Miss E. M. Robinson.

The Band of Help is doing excellent work, this being a society of children, each undertaking to pay at least a penny a month towards the cost of a Woodland's Bed. At that time there were but five Band of Help Beds, one from King Edward's Grammar School for Girls, Bath Row, one from Harborne, one from Sutton Coldfield, and two by all other branches. The first private bed endowment, to Woodlands, had been given by Mrs and Miss Robins, in memory of the late W.H.Robins.

Further information re the Chadwick End Home is given in Chapter 5.

At that 11th Annual Meeting a name change was announced, from 'Crippled Childrens Union' to the 'Cripples Union' and Frank Mathews sets out to put the role of the work of the Woodlands into perspective with that of the Cripple's Union:- "... some friends seem to have but a hazy idea of the work that is being done, and that it is merely that undertaken by our children's Nursing Home. Although the Woodlands is, and will be, an increasingly important factor in the success of the work, that which has to be done before and after patients enter the Home is equally indispensable". He re-states those early principles upon which the Union had been founded; 'full particulars to be taken'; 'home conditions investigated'; ' visiting every home'; 'advice as to diet, open-air, on return from convalescent treatment etc. "... we are able to see that the health gained is not lost through carelessness or ignorance". In modern terms he is saying ' The Woodlands is a means to an end, not the end in itself '.

Life for the children within the Woodlands, however gives him much pleasure. "... the keynote is joyousness, happiness, both summer and winter. Anyone standing outside the wards, and hearing the sound within, would find it difficult to believe that it came from 30 of the worst crippled children of the city . ... I have been surprised that the children, coming as they do, from hot and air-less homes, have not objected to the open-air treatment. ... the construction of the place has proved most suitable ... the verandah with its slope leading to the garden below, enables every child, whether in bed or spinal carriage, to be taken down at a moments notice. Keen interest is taken in the Hay-fields and the surrounding country-side.

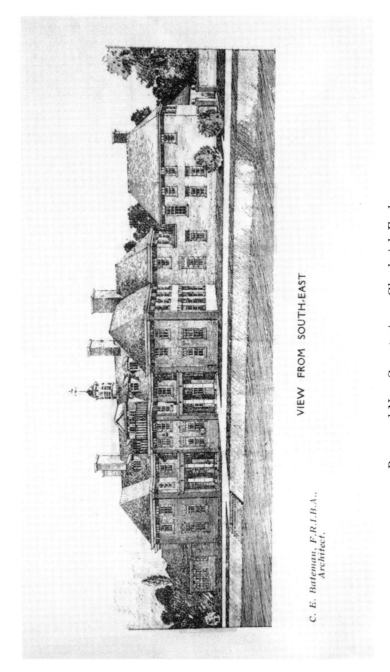

VIEW FROM SOUTH-EAST

C. E. Bateman, F.R.I.B.A.,
Architect.

Proposed New Sanatorium, Chadwick End
Source: Crippled Children's Union. Annual Reports 1900-1908
photo: Brian Jones

One small boy, seeing the cows in a near field, remarked ' it was the first time he'd seen a cow 'cept a wild one in our street' ". (he would have witnessed the cows being driven to slaughter through the city centre streets).

Miss L. Rose, was appointed Matron in 1911 (from the Royal Orthopaedic Hospital, London), following the resignation of Miss Robinson. The Home-work, in the capable hands of the Handicraft Teachers, Miss Thomas, Miss Lloyd and Miss Hawkes, had seen the training of 45 cripples (in their homes) during the year. Whilst the Secretary gives thanks (without any mention of his role as organiser) to the helpers at the summer party at the Manor Farm, taking all the helpless little children. Two furniture vans being chartered to take their carriages. "... many of the boys paddled in the Brook, were told they 'might not' splash. One was later found wet, they weren't splashing, but 'playing football' in the brook. It is the only place where children with crutches, with a paralysed foot, with a splint on, can safely have a half-hours paddle". The facilities were also available to the adult cripples.

During 1912, some 76 children had been at the Woodlands for long periods, and 48 for a three-weeks stay, the treatment being so successful that many of them had been able to go straight to ordinary Council Schools, and some having been ordered by their doctor to remove their instruments. It is also recorded that "... The Committee meets every month under the chairmanship of Mrs. George Cadbury, all domestic details coming under their notice". The Daily Mail Fund enabled the opening of a further six beds.

1913-14, shows an increase of beds to 60, and 137 patients passing through, 50 for three weeks, remainder for longer treatment, 38 returning home the majority cured. This year marks a milestone in the educational side of the Woodlands, with the founding of its school. "... We are glad to record that the Birminghnam Education Committee have provided a teacher, and also appliances, giving the children an hours lesson every day. This has been a very great pleasure to our children, but is, we are afraid, too short to be of any real educational value. We hope it is only a beginning, and that as time goes on the Education Committee will see their way to appoint another teacher, so that the time spent may be of greater educational value.

I am most indebted to Mrs Ann Baxter, the (present) teacher in charge (1997) for the following extract, commencing May 1914

May 1st   School commenced today
            Annie A. King.   Head Mistress.
            Mildred Margerison.   Assistant Mistress.
            Jessie Bull.   Assistant Mistress.

May 18th   New Stock arrived today.

May 22nd   The attendance has been very good indeed, only one pupil absent at all, and this absence is occasioned by an operation

May 29th   School closes today for the Whitsuntide holidays. Mrs. Marsh visited the school this morning.

June 8th   Work is resumed today after the Whitsun holidays.

June 10th   There is some alteration in the time-table today on account of an "At Home" held at Woodlands.

June 25th   The registers were checked this morning by Mrs. Marsh on her visit to the school.

July 1st   The School Committee met at Woodlands today.

    Presented at Committee Meeting   July 1st 1914.
    and signed by:-   *Eliz. M. Cadbury.*

Note:- There exists a fascinating booklet entitled:-
*'Landmarks in the History of the Woodlands Hospital School, 1914-1996',
by Mrs Ann Brown, the Head Mistress at the time of its closure, containing extracts from every year, of the Woodlands School Log Books, ending on July 19th, 1996. and with a defiant statement of pride:-*
"... the caring ethos which was evident in 1914 will continue in the seperate Centres providing a solid foundation for making future educational provision in hospital".
and ending .... the story will continue.

The Woodland's Needlework Guild is recorded as having a membership of 70 ladies who had kindly made over 150 garments for children at Woodlands. Moving back to the Union's Administration at Newhall Street, the Office School is proving to be a most useful source of employment, having been used for some 14 years as a school of shorthand and typing for crippled girls. Four girls are earning £1 a week, non having worked for less that 10/- a week.

There are many 'friends' making gifts to the Woodlands throughout each year. It is not surprising to find George (and Elizabeth) Cadbury amongst them, the humble and caring side of the man willing to spend Thousands of pounds on one hand and yet never forgetting the children's (and staff) immediate needs:- for tickets for a display at Bournville; for weekly gifts of chocolates; woollen jerseys for the nurses; storm curtains for the wards, and, a gift of a Goldfish.

*Mr. Naughton Dunn. Honorary Surgeon, appears for the first time in the 15th Annual Report, in 1915. Whilst the death of Mr. Jordan Lloyd is recorded, he having been Hon. Surgeon since the founding of the Society. *(An individual story of the life and work of Naughton Dunn will be found in Chapter 6). George Cadbury is "... thanked for adding to his kindness to us, the gift of a new ward, verandah and garden, together with a nurse's and servant's bedrooms ... increasing our accomodation by at least 14 beds."

The Union Offices were moved to Daimler House, Paradise Street, a long time need, so enabling a seperate room for the shorthand school, and providing proper accommodation for Secretaries, visiting staff and clerks. The growth of the Society was such that Mr. Mathews Assistant (Miss Cox) was promoted to Co- Secretary.

The school is reorganised during 1915. "... At the present time almost all the over-five years are having several hours of school daily ... the school has received recognition as a Special Open-Air School for defective children by the Board of Education, who are making substantial grants, towards the cost of Education, Maintenance and Medical-treatment. The children are taught a variety of subjects, including singing, gardening-work and handwork".

Following the appointment of Mr. Dunn, and under his drive, a conservatory was adapted as an operating theatre. (The cost of £300 being defrayed by the Feeney Trustees,), and during the year he had performed 22 operations. "No doubt a great many more would have been done had it not been for the war, but two operation Sisters subsequently left us to nurse wounded soldiers, and we had great difficulty in filling their places". Mr. Dunn had also been holding Clinics at Daimler House, and was using instruments made in "our own" workshops.

Even by this time the facilities at Woodlands were proving inadequate, and additional convalescent and boarding-out work was being envisaged. "... The amount spent on this work increases year by year, as there are quite a number of children who, even after a long stay at Woodlands, still need a few months in the country ... There are others who are not ill enough to go to Woodlands and need some months, occasionally years, in the country to aid and complete their cure. ... We are considering the advisability of starting an Open-Air Sanatorium School in the country. ... The scheme has received approval and the Committee are looking for a site and for £1,000 which will build and equip a Sanatorium. ..."

There is more on the School in 1916, when the curriculum is said to be that of ordinary schools, but with greater attention given to hand work, such as; occupations for the younger children, plain and fancy needle work, leather work, raffia work, pen painting, pastinello, and drawing for the older ones. The children selling their work to visitors, making £20, this being expended in the purchase of a sewing machine. The Board of Education had arranged for very young children to have a teacher during the morning, the fact that this was not covered by the Board scheme was balanced by the advantages of having them occupied, both for the sake of their training and for the quietness and order of school.

Mr. Naughton Dunn offered his services to the R.A.M.C. and Miss Hunt, (by arragement with Mr. Dunn), of the Baschurch Surgical and Nursing Home carried on his clinic.

The break down of the cost of running the Woodlands for the year ending 31st March 1916 is interesting:-

Salaries and Wages.   £844   8   11

Rent, Rates, Taxes, Insurance
Telephone.   133 1 11
Coal, Light, Water.   202 5 8
Provisions.   852 3 0
Travelling and Pony.   37 2 5.$\frac{1}{2}$
Washing and Labour.   155 0 1.$\frac{1}{2}$
Carriage, Postages etc.   42 9 4
Printing, Stationary etc.   42 19 0
Medicine, Surgical Instruments
Dressings etc.   125 16 3
Bank Charges.   36 19 7
Furniture and Household Goods.   32 19 9
Clothing, Bedding etc.   46 19 4.$\frac{1}{2}$
Repairs and Renewals.   24 14 4
Sundries.   11 18 10   £2,588 15 6.$\frac{1}{2}$

To Education.
Teachers Salaries.   269 3 4
Secretary to Managers   50 0 0
Furniture   5 5 0
Books, Stationary etc.   49 11 11
                                        374 0 2   £2,962 15 8.$\frac{1}{2}$

There has been movement towards a new scheme for a Convalescent Home and School of Recovery which in 1917, "... had to be shelved owing to building restrictions". *(presumably war-time!)*.The following year it is stated "...We shall be ready to commence building as soon as restrictions on building are removed, for we are glad to report that a friend (who prefers to remain under the anonymous title 'A Theosophist'), has sold his house for £2,500, and an appeal to subscribers in the summer brought us about £700. The Committee appears to be searching around numerous sites.

A qualified Recreation Teacher had been appointed, at Woodlands, to enable the children to make the most of their leisure time, involving roaming around the grounds; driven in a pony drawn Trap exploring country lanes; visits to Birmingham Art Gallery; buying and keeping rabbits; guinea pigs and a donkey., also interest in a library.

A comparison of costs and facilities is made for the two years 1911 and 1918, when, with the numbers treated being practically the same 1,319;1,400 respectively. the spending had increased four-fold.

	1911	1918
Spending	£3,472.	£12,256.
Beds	45	95
	£1,175	£6,041.
	No education	5 teachers. £742 spent on education. Grant of £1,700.

Surgical Appliances.

	£55.	£885.

Spinal Carriages

	£62.	£158.

Money spent on children's convalescent work entirely apart from Woodlands;

	£62.	£1,760.

An addition was made on the suggestion of Major Naughton Dunn and Miss Hunt, with the appointment of Miss Cook to take charge of the afternoon clinic. Miss Hunt having taken over as Superintendent of all his cases.

The 21st Annual Report of the Cripple's Union (1919-20) announces the help being offered by the Birmingham Mail 'Xmas Tree Fund, and particularly the efforts of Mr. H.F.Harvey its Editor. The preamble acknowledges the help given, over the years, re 'special developments' and 'opening of beds'. Mr. Harvey is now involved in future developments regarding the need for a new convalescent home which it was believed could be bought for about £12,000, and he offered to help raise the necessary Funds.

I am most indebted to Mr. Roy Calfield for the following information:-

" MAIL " XMAS TREE FUND
" MAIL " OFFICE, CORPORATION STREET.

BIRMINGHAM. November 27th, 1919.

Dear Sir (or Madam),

We are making a special appeal this year in connection with our Fund, and invite your earnest consideration and support.

The Birmingham Cripple's Union is in urgent need of a new Convalescent Home to relieve congestion at the Woodlands, and to permit the treatment of many sad cases of crippled children for whom no adequate provision or treatment can now be made. It has been made clear to us that if such a Home was provided many afflicted children would be cured who otherwise must become permanently deformed, their lives a burden to themselves and to the community. We have therefore undertaken to assist the Cripple's Union in raising a building fund ...

At the same time we must raise the money for providing boots and clothing and entertainments for poor children, summer holidays for war orphans, Christmas presents for war pensioners in local hospitals, and Christmas dinners and coal for the necessitous families of our city.

We trust you will mark your approval of our appeal by forwarding a contribution. If you desire to earmark any special sum for the Crippled Children's home we shall be glad to carry out your wishes.

Yours faithfully

H. F. Harvey, Hon. Treasurer

It is hardly surprising that £14,000 was raised by the beginning of January, 1920, and with the £2,500 already in hand, together with £416 from additional subscribers, all seemed well, until it was discovered that the lowest cost for such a building would be £30,000.

Now for two slight diversions; Notice was given to the Union, in 1919, with the Corporation proposing to apply to Parliament for power to acquire a strip in front of the Woodlands for road widening purposes (the dual carriage-way!), in connection with the proposed Tramway along the Bristol Road. (Trams to the Lickeys, Rednal, and Rubery) and also, £100 has been given by Mr. Samuelson (Uncle John of the Weekly Post) for the provision of holidays for 50 convalescent children.

Returning to concern for a convalescent home. A site at Tanworth-in-Arden being under consideration for which 'The Projected Convalescent Home for Crippled Children' plans produced by the firm of Architects, Messrs Harvey and Wicks, show a completely circular design, all of the open-air-wards facing inwards in an arc, with the administration and isolation block and a caretakers cottage, facing diametrically opposite. Accommodation being for 80 children. Another proposal was an extension of the Woodlands, George Cadbury having intimated his willingness to give whatever further land was necessary, free of cost to the Union. At this time a property came on the market, the 'Forelands' a house previously tenanted by Sir John Middlemore, at Rock Hill, a little South of Bromsgrove town centre. 171/2 acres of land was purchased using the Xmas Tree monies, and it was proposed to build two open-air wards, and an open-air schoolroom for 80 children. "... it having the great advantage that it can almost immediately be occupied as a convalescent home , by a certain number of children while the dormiteries etc., are being built ...".

The Committee also advised that Messrs. Weaver and Bunn, who had been in the employ of Sir John Middlemore, be taken on as gardeners, Weaver at 55/- weekly and the Lodge; Bunn at 50/- weekly and cottage.

The administrative facilities at Daimler House are causing concern. The staff being inadequate and no chance of expanding. The orthopaedic clinic under Naughton Dunn was developing, having taken on a trained Orthopaedic Assistant, Masseuse and Assistant Masseuse. Only 250 cases out of 1,130 on the books, are being treated. The clinic arose from the original work of the Union, whence Visiting, Supervision, Employment, Convalescence, Education are still the by-words, and the supplying of notes, not just for the orthopaedic hospital, but also Eye Hospital; Ear and Throat notes, together with the need to 'keep the mother well, and constantly supply Dispensary notes for this purpose'. Alterations costing some £3,000 are being called for at the Woodlands, no fewer than 104 beds occupied, urgent waiting lists, never below three, generally nine to thirteen for tubercular cases alone, exclusive of children waiting for operative treatment.

The Union's General Committee announces (in May 1920), a request from the Orthopaedic Hospital for closer co-operation, resulting in an informal conference. Further meetings had been held and by September a 'Report was being prepared'.

The 1921, Twenty-Second Annual Report makes the first reference to, the now, functioning 'Forelands', (Staff had taken residence on the 19th October and the first batch of children, (24), admitted 2nd November), as the Open-Air School of Recovery, Bromsgrove. The Honorary Medical Officer being W. H. Rowlands, and Mr. F. Wilson Stuart as additional surgeon to Mr. Naughton Dunn. The report states "... We have never experienced a more anxious year than the last, for at one period we were spending considerably more than we were getting, and had to make drastic revision ... The Visiting staff were cut down; all extra nourishments to home cases stopped; nearly all convalescent work other than Woodlands and Forelands had to cease; adult entertainments were given up, and for a time 'no less than twenty three beds' were closed at the Woodlands".

The good news comes that fortunately income had now, increased "... at a much greater rate than we dared hope ... and we have finished the year with a level balance sheet".

Concern is being expressed for children suffering from tubercular bone disease, initially in terms of an anomoly regarding the cost of treatment, which in the surrounding counties and districts to Birmingham, is provided free, whereas in Birmingham the chance of cure is dependant "... for most part on the very uncertain income of charity ... We have a great number of paralysed and rickety children ... The treatment of tubercular bone disease must come first as being appallingly wasteful and terribly painful if left unattended, and so long as we receive no help financially for our tubercular bone cases, equally important cases of deformity from paralysis and rickets have to remain un-helped".

The necessity for the Forelands is again stressed. 'To cure a child suffering from bone-disease, so as to prevent all deformity and to make practically sure of there being no benign relapse is said to require at least £150, to be spent in a Sanatorium, followed by expensive after-care for three to five years.' Further generosity from the Xmas Tree Fund had brought in £1,168, but to thoroughly equip and complete the Forelands

Commemoration Plaque
Birmingham Mail X'mas Tree Fund £15,000 for the 'Forelands'
Source: R.T.C photo: Brian Jones

Official Opening 'The Forelands'
Source: R.T.C photo: Brian Jones

Forelands: Interests in pigeons & poultry
&
the school has its own tuck-shop

£22,000 would be needed, an application was made to the Ministry of Health, and after the house, site, and plans had been inspected and approved by them, they agreed to provide three-fifths of the cost providing the City Council would agree to carry on the home for thirty years as a Sanatorium for the treatment of tubercular bone disease, in the event of the Society being unable to do so.

The Health Committee (of the Council) agreed to this and the Society was then expecting to receive £14,000, and then using some of the money from the Mail Fund, for maintaining the home, during the year. The first batch of 40 children entered Forelands in November 1921, (It had been formally opened on October 5th, 1921, by the Lord Mayor and Lady Mayoress [of Birmingham], Alderman and Mrs. W.A.Cadbury), all suffering from tubercular bone disease, and ".. we are trying to give them interests that will take them out of doors in later life, Gardening; games; nature study; country walks and drives; the care of pets such as rabbits, pigeons and pigs".

The school has its own tuck-shop, the children assisted by the staff purchasing the stock, dealing with the traveller and keeping a profit and loss account. The same being done with the poultry and pigs.

It was referred to earlier, that twenty-three beds had been closed, this was reduced to twenty-one by the kindness of the Misses Jenkins offer to support two beds for a year, also, thanks to the generosity of the women employees of Messrs. Cadbury Bros. all the beds were re-opened as they are making a weekly collection for us, so guaranteeing £700 pa.. Employees of Cadbury's, at the Beeches, another Cadbury home, undertook the whole cost of maintaining a bed at Woodlands, through the Band of Help.

A sad event is recorded in 1922 the resignation of Mr. Frank Mathews as Organising Secretary and his departure from the Crippled Children's Union, what surely has to be considered 'His Union'. The Committee announce 'with profound regret, his resignation after Twenty-five years service in the cause of crippled children in Birmingham'.

Mr. Mathews letter of resignation, reads:-

"Maple Road, Bournville, Birmingham. January 3rd, 1922.

Dear Miss Rolason

You will remember that I wrote you in August 1920, saying that I was contemplating giving up the work of the Cripple's Union. The matter has never been out of my mind since and today I have come to the decision that the present is far by the best time for me to send in my resignation. The Committee are about to consider a new policy ... which I can by no means whole heartedly accept. I quite appreciate the Committee's difficulty and cannot say that I have an alternative to suggest, although had these alterations, in a modified form, been spread over several years, I might have been able to accept them.

I am very anxious that the Committee should believe that I do not wish to dictate in anyway, or to be unreasonable. But the work having developed so rapidly of late, bringing with it greater strain and responsibility, I feel that if the conditions under which the work is continued are to become more difficult, that I could not stand any further strain. The only means by which I have been able to continue the work of late has been by making constant breaks, with very unsatisfactory results.

I feel that I have given 25 years of very arduous service to the Society and that now I should be set free to do a similar work on a smaller scale in some other part of the country should opportunity offer. In my opinion the Union is so well organised that it can quite well afford to do without me.

Sincerely yours Frank Mathews".

(The contents of this letter beg clarification. however, at this stage I will delay stating the complete story, particularly as it moves outside of this history. Frank did not lose contact and, as will be seen later, returned to the fold in 1947, however in view of the public response to my inquiry as to why and what Frank subsequently did, this will appear in Chapter 5).

The Committee gives the following glowing testimony "The result such as he achieved is a record which no other man or woman has equalled. He founded the Cripple's Union, and in spite of untold difficulties in the early days kept the Society going. Recall for a moment the tiny organisation visiting a handful of children, with a precarious income, without trained helpers or Institutions of any kind, and then look at the Society at the present time, with a Hospital, a Convalescent School and Outpatient's

Clinic, a large staff of trained Visitors, workshops, and all the many branches of activity which the Union is engaged upon, and one must realise the immense store of energy, devotion, and untiring work which must have been given by the man who made all this possible. No expression of thanks or appreciation can be adequate, and knowing Mr. Mathews, we feel sure he would be the last person to desire such tributes. ... as long as work for Crippled Children endures, his name will be remembered in connection with it. We wish him every success in his new work ... wherever he may be, the lot of Cripples will be made easier and work on their behalf go forward". (This article was written by Miss Christine Cox who had been for many years Frank's joint-secretary).

Mr. H. F. Harvey, who has played such an important role in fund-raising for the Cripple's Union was appointed Chairman of the Union, during the year, having been introduced to it by Frank Mathews two years previously. He is to play an even greater role in the period up to the 1925 amalgamation, and for the following 23 years.

The year 1921-22 marks progress, at Woodlands, with the provision of new and up-to-date massage, electrical and plaster room; a gymnasium and X-ray rooms, together with a bungalow for the resident Home Surgeon, additional Nurses quarters and an Isolation block. (this being installed in the former coal cellar and coach house) George Cadbury, again, gave £1,000, also the Feeney Trust and Birmingham Mail Xmas Tree Fund, towards the cost of improvements. The X-ray apparatus, (second hand) was obtained by Dr. James Brailsford (who had been appointed as radiographer on the 1st January 1922), and fitted up in converted rooms.

The children at the Forelands, boys and girls, are helping with sweeping, dusting and general housework, learning cobbling and carpentry and helping in poultry work. An early success is stated for 'Our head boy' who having been under treatment for a number of years with an acute tubercular hip, has the promise of employment, locally. The Scouts and Guides are prospering, Mr. Hedges the Bromsgrove Scoutmaster coming in every week, and the Mistresses and Nurses enthusiastic in Guides.

It was on "a pouring day in August last (1921)", that Daimler House was vacated "... what had seemed to be palatial premises in 1914 had become utterly unsuitable and inadequate". The new Administrative premises being at 42-44 Islington Row. Information is given re the ' Carriage Depot and Workshops' having been moved in from Theodore Street, and that the work is being carried out on the spot, so avoiding delay. All the workers in the splint and boot shops, with the exception of the head mechanic, being ex-patients, and the leather work is done by crippled girls.

There is great satisfaction at Forelands with the fact that "... two of the older boys are now employed, on the staff, one in the garden, the other in the boot repair shop (having trained in the Islington Row workshop)".

Trees are being felled and storm water drains laid for the widening of the Bristol Road for the tramway. "... a considerable piece of land in front of the Woodlands ..." having been given to the Council.

The Woodlands has appointed Dr. Lewis as House Surgeon taking up his duties on 3rd June 1922, and Miss Margurite Cook appointed Sister Tutor in charge of the Massage and Gymnasium on July 5th. The Bungalow is now completed and the Isolation Block in the process of erection.

On the 1st August 1922, the General Committee Chairman (Mr. H. F. Harvey) reports that they had been approached by the Orthopaedic Hospital with regard to the possibility of erecting a ward for 30 patients (women and children) adjoining the Woodlands. Negotiations had taken place.

All such events were over shadowed by the death of George Cadbury on the 24th October 1922. Mrs. George Cadbury in response to the Union's letter of condolence, is so touching:-

"Mrs. George Cadbury and her family desire to thank you and the Society that you represent, very sincerely for your kind thoughts and sympathy; also for expressing your appreciation of the character, work and simplicity of life of one whose practical devotion to the needs of the world was inspired by a corresponding devotion to his interpretation of the will of God.

In this dark hour of history, when men are reaching for truth and a living faith, may it not be an inspiration to know that the secret of his life was the belief in the reality of God as a Father in the ultimate triumph of goodness., and in a vision of the Divine in every man, a faith that was upheld by communion with the Unseen".

The pulling down of the Old Lodge, (due to the widening of Bristol Road) and the building of a new Lodge has been considered as at January 1923, with Compensation from the Council, at a cost of £725. to commence immediately. *This was completed 3 months later.*

Negotiations with the Orthopaedic Hospital are far from reaching a satisfactory completion, with frustration being shown (on both sides) and, indeed in October 1923, "... after negotiations extending over three years... no useful purpose can be served by continuing... recommend they be brought to a conclusion". (Negotiations were called off the following month).

Sister Kennedy having left on October 1st 1923, Sister Smith has been appointed Sister-in-Charge. (a Matron in waiting!)

The next Annual Report of the Birmingham Cripple's Union applauds the success of the 'Office School' in giving good business training, free of charge to crippled girls. Also 'A matinee of the Italian Circus had been put on at the Alexandra Theatre on July 8th, 1924, to which over 600 crippled children had been invited'. I mention this because of the organisation that had arranged it, 'The Rocket Club'. This club itself celebrates its Centenary in October 1997, so running parallel with the Cripples Union, and it had over the years endowed many beds, and named a Ward, all at the Forelands. (Detail of this is given in Chapter 5).

On 5th February 1925, was announced the subsequent success of negotiations, when Mr. Harvey, Chairman of the Cripples Union, and Miss Cox, the General Secretary, reported on the proposed Merger. To be called "The Birmingham Cripples Union and Royal Orthopaedic and Spinal Hospital (Amalgamated). Sir Gilbert Barling to be the Chairman for the first year, and it was explained that the Orthopaedic Hospital had the sum of £32,000 for Building purposes, and that it was hoped to purchase the Old Children's Hospital in Broad Street to be opened as a Clinic. (At this time it was still being thought that "...in a few years time, Highbury might become available").

On to Amalgamation

MR. H. F. HARVEY.
Editor Birmingham Mail 1907 - 1944
Source: Souvenir Programme 1929, Opening of New Buildings R.T.C.

Chapter 3

Amalgamation
1925 -1928

The Birmingham Cripples Union and
Royal Orthopaedic and Spinal Hospital (Amalgamated) had as its Officers
and Committee, at its formation:-

President: Lord Ednam, M.C

Chairman: Sir Gilbert Barling; Bart.

Vice-Chairmen : J. H. Francis, O.B.E. : H.F.Harvey.

Hon. Treasurers: Mrs. Gerald Kenrick; Clive J. Levi.

Hon. Secretaries: Miss Rolason; Frank G. Stephens.

Committee : *(inclusive of above, other than the President)*

Miss Barrows	H.T.Buckland	Mrs. George Cadbury, O.B.E.
Laurence Cadbury	C. Chambers	Naughton Dunn*
Edward Evershed	W.T.Fairfax	Mrs. E.M.Gibson
Stephen Godlee	Mrs. Howard Heaton	George Jackson, J.P.
J.B.Leather*	Mrs. Marsh	G.P.Mills*
J.Morris	Arthur Rabone, J.P.	Hugh P. Raikes
Capt. L.M.Ryland	Miss Sergant	L. Arthur Smith
Charles A. Smith	F. Wilson Stuart*	Allan Tangye
Fred. Venimore	John Weatherhead	W. H. Williams, O.B.E.

Additional Medical and Surgical Staff (*to the four above named) being:-
T.L.Hardy; H.Guy Dain; W.H.Rowlands; Walter R.Jordan and S.A McPhee.

General Secretary: Miss Christine Cox;

Assistant Secretary: Miss Irene Whittock

Finance Secretary; Miss Frances B. Evans.

The Offices being at 42-44 Islington Row.

(a close look at these names would show a more or less 50/50 representation from each of the amalgamating institutions, the agreed format to carry through for the first year).

The Amalgamation was to take place as from March 31st, 1925, however for this history I feel it is worth looking back, at the negotiations taking place within the Joint Negotiating Committee. This material being directly from the Amalgamation Minutes, December 1924 - February 1925.

A Conference of Representatives of the two institutions was held on 2nd December 1924, at which it is seen that both the Ministry of Health and Board of Education were very much behind the need for Amalgamation. Calling for the re-opening of negotiations "... the Orthopaedic Hospital and Cripples Union are providing a similar service and to a certain extent overlap ... They stress that Birmingham is the most convenient place for the treatment of tubercular bone cases and cripples, for outside areas, on the most efficient and economical lines." The roles of the individual Institutions are re-stated. "...The Orthopaedic Hospital deals with children and adults, taking its patients also from outside areas, whereas the Cripples Union has limited its work almost exclusively to the city ... The Cripples Union was maintaining 180 beds at the Woodlands; Forelands Open-air School and Convalescent Home, with an outpatient department at Islington Row... Provision, at an early date, for very young (1 to 5 years) was necessary.... The Newhall Street Orthopaedic Hospital had 40 beds and had acquired an additional 30 beds at Vicarage Road as a temporary provision. Highbury and Uffculme (Richard Cadbury's former home) were uncertain Orthopaedic facilities".

The resolutions passed at this conference included; Five representatives of each Institution be appointed to a Joint Negotiating Committee; a sub-committee consisting of not more than two representatives from each side be charged with the preliminary task of drafting proposals. 14 days later the first J.N.C. reported, the Drafting Committee consisting of Mrs. George Cadbury; H.F.Harvey and C.T.Levi having submitted a report agreeing the new title and:-

"The complete pooling of all buildings, equipment, financial resources and a union of the staffs ... Control to be exercised by an executive committee composed, at the outset, of the existing General Committee of the Orthopaedic Hospital and the executive and finance committee of the Cripples Union, with Sir Gilbert Barling as Chairman and the two present

Chairmen as Deputy Chairman ... The Hon. Officers; Hon. Treasurers and Hon. Secretaries of the two Institutions to serve for the first twelve months. ... The Finance Committee to be composed of three representatives of each Institution with the Chairman of the Executive Committee, the Hon. Officers and Chairman of the House Committee of the Orthopaedic Hospital, Woodlands and Forelands, ex-officio ... Four representatives of the Orthopaedic Hospital to be added to the Woodlands House Committee and two to the Forelands ... with two representatives of the Cripples Union added to the Orthopaedic House Committee". After the first year there was to be no further distinction, representation on all Committees being by the rules of normal election".

The Medical Board was to comprise all the members of the Medical and Surgical Staff. General Meetings were to be held periodically and to include 'ladies and gentlemen' not members of committees but who are active voluntary workers for either Institution, as Annual Subscribers of £2-2-0 upwards, representatives of workers auxiliaries and of Works which collect sums of £10 upwards.

The Orthopaedic Hospital is to be continued as at present, but with the intention of it, eventually, being reserved for adults and persons over 14 years of age. Vicarage Road is to be equipped as a Convalescent and Treatment Centre for cases cleared from the Orthopaedic Hospital and controlled by the O.H. House Committee. Forelands to continue as a Tubercular Bone Tumour Convalescent School. Outpatient Departments are to continue at the present centres but there were hopes for the opening of more clinics. The proposed purchase of the Broad Street Hospital was approved; as was (this is news) the establishment by the Cripples Union of a Children's Clinic at Coventry.

On the 13th February 1925 a joint sub-committee was set up, inviting 2 nominations from each Institution, to prepare Draft Laws and Bye-Laws for the Government of the Amalgamated Hospital, also 2 representatives for a Staff and Office Organisation Sub-committee. A further representation being called for the Hospital re-organisation sub-committee to consider the matters relating to Clinics, Workshops, and Nurses Training Scheme.

It was at this February 1925 meeting that " ... the Secretary was asked to undertake the preparation of a booklet giving information of the history and work of the Institutions for circulation among old and new subscribers..." This eleven page history was published in 1926.

The approval of the Scheme for Amalgamation was given by the Subscriber's to the Cripple's Union, at a meeting held on Thursday, February 19th, 1925, the Orthopaedic Hospital Subscribers six days later.

The First Executive Committee was held, at the Chamber of Commerce, on Thursday 5th March 1925, at which "... Instruction was given to the Hon. Secretaries (of the two Institutions) ... at once to give formal notice to all (their) members that their service under the existing agreements will terminate and at the same time to intimate to such persons that in the event of their having no objection to the transfer of their services they will be deemed to be members of the Birmingham Cripples Union and Royal Orthopaedic and Spinal Hospital (Amalgamated), as from 31st March, 1925, on the same terms and conditions as before".

Two reports follow on the 4th May, 1925, from Mr.J.H.Francis, on behalf of the Orthopaedic Institution and Mr. H.F.Harvey for the Cripple's Union. The purchase of the Broad Street Hospital had been completed. (and the Newhall Street House Committee having been authorised to proceed with its re-decoration) £66 spent on Electric Apparatus, and on Furniture £94. A Central Heating estimate of £300 had been accepted. Alterations at Vicarage Road were in hand, and the Newhall Street House Committee were to furnish same.

Mr. Harvey reported extensive repairs to the drainage at Islington Row.

The Joint Sub-committee dealing with Hospitals, Clinics and Workshops, reported Hospital Policy. Vicarage Road to be regarded as a Treatment Centre for non-operative bed-cases, over 16 years of age; Woodlands reserved, as far as possible, for cases between 2 and 16 years of age, with Forelands being retained as a Convalescence School for Tubercular Bone Cases, under 16 years of age, both sexes. Steps to be taken to maintain continuity of treatment by the same Surgeon in whichever Institute the patient happens to be.

There is to be a gradual transfer of patients, from Newhall Street and

Islington Row, to Broad Street, requiring massage and electrical treatment. Dr. McPhee, having his appointment extended, taking charge of the department.

Now at last! "The ticket system to be abolished ... A notification be sent to all subscribers informing them of the change and appealing for continued support ..." A further suggestion made, was that a special form should be available for Subscribers wishing personally to recommend a case, which could be procured from the Hospital. (a meeting was to be held, on 23rd June 1925, to explain the abolition to all subscribers and voluntary workers).

Enquiries were coming in from surrounding area Councils; Worcestershire, Smethwick Cripple's Union; Nuneaton with regard to establishing Orthopaedic Clinics in their areas. (Extern Clinics).

The Book-keeping system was to be amalgamated as from 31st July, 1925 "... by which time new books can be obtained and the system adjusted between the two hospitals." Accommodation is soon at a premium, when a call goes out that "... additional beds are urgently required ... desirable that steps be taken to approach the Highbury Trustees ...". Alterations are recommended for the provision of new X-ray apparatus, at the Woodlands, the cost, estimated at £670, being partially covered by a gift to the Cripples Union of £500. Broad Street is also looking for £890 for Radiography equipment, and an additional £200 pa., as the stipend, for an operator and supervision by an expert Radiographer with Medical Qualifications.

Salaries and allowances are connected at Newhall Street, and with the proposed move to Broad Street, as the following considerations show; "Salaries paid to the Massage Department at Newhall Street and Islington Row have been compared, and it is estimated that taking into consideration the fact that the Newhall Street staff have dinner, tea, uniform and laundry provided, the scale of salaries is about equal. It is suggested that when the department is moved to Broad Street and free meals discontinued, an addition of £30 should be made to the Newhall Street salaries in lieu of meals, uniform and laundry which will cease to be applied. Meals, lunch and tea may be supplied to the Staff at a cost of 1/- , and 6d for cups of tea.

Miss Hadley, as Matron at Woodlands has control over Vicarage Road and Miss Horsley is appointed Sister-in-Charge. and the loss of the Note system has created a few difficulties "... it is desirable to emphasise that before being admitted to Vicarage Road or Newhall Street, cases should be interviewed and particulars taken".

The Training of Nurses is stated as consisting of two years as Orthopaedic Probation Nurses, followed by another two years either General Training, at a recognised General Hospital, (the second year only for an O.P nurse), so hopefully returning to orthopaedic nursing. Alternatively the last two years could be 'Training for the Swedish Remedial Exercises', leading to the Chartered Society of Massage and Medical Gymnastic Certificate, thus suiting them to orthopaedic After-Care nursing. Matrons of Recognised General Hospitals in Birmingham were to be consulted as to whether this scheme would receive their support.

The Outpatient and Operating Duties of the Hon. Surgeons and Anaesthetists were listed.

Outpatient Afternoons:-

Monday	Mr. Wilson Stuart.	Tuesday	Mr.Percival Mills.
Wednesday	Mr. J.B.Leather.	Thursday	Mr. Naughton Dunn.
Friday	Mr. Percival Mills.		

Operation Mornings:-

Day	Surgeon	Anaesthetist
Tuesday	Mr. Mills.	Dr. Walter Jordan.
Wednesday	Mr. Leather.	Dr. Walter Jordan.
Thursday	Mr. Stuart.	Dr. Bernard Wall.
Friday	Mr. Naughton Dunn.	Dr. Helen Fox. (temporarily)

Following on from the outside requests for the forming of Extern Orthopaedic Clinics, a Form was sent, outlining the Rules. Cripples from E.O.Clinics can be treated as inpatients and outpatients at the existing Hospitals and Clinics, so far as accommodation permits; (no reservation of beds, at present, but hope to increase number of beds for this purpose). All charges as agreed by the Ministry, exclusive of apparatus; Supervision of the Externs' by an Orthopaedic Surgeon, a scheme being instituted for After-Care Nurses to attend regularly; Surgeon's Fee £3-3-0 minimum per

11/2 hr. session, plus travelling. Charge for a part-time nurse based on amount of time spent.

Overall changes in staffing and responsibilities, in line with the Amalgamation rules, are now stated. This information I include, for the record and interest, in that it acts as an Index of the staff of the day.

The Report from the Staff and Office Sub-Committee announces that Islington Row will be the Headquarters with Miss Cox, General Secretary; Miss Whittock, Assistant Secretary and Mr. Dutton, Accountant and Clerk to the Finance Committee. To remain at Newhall Street are, Miss Witt and Miss Lavell, also doing clerical work for Vicarage Road; Miss Stephens, Miss Maxwell and the Almoner Miss Mountford. Miss Johnson to attend at Broad Street Treatment Department, and Miss Little when the Doctor's begin to see outpatients.

Reference has been made to changes in 'Free meals', the next statement however seems to go one step further. "All meals to the Staff should be stopped and their salaries reconsidered".

The Shorthand School and Correspondence Department, remains in the control of Miss West, and Miss Florence Tony, at present a Pupil, to be employed as an assistant at 10/- weekly. The abolition of the Ticket system again requires changes by the Case-Papers Department, in assessment of payments, it being recommended that the Islington Row system be used, Orthopaedic tickets offered by applicants being taken, their value being assessed at 5/3d cash. Miss Whittock is to organise this department, with the assistance of Miss Taylor, (presently employed as a Social Visitor).

In August 1925 hopes for the use of Highbury are at last dashed. "... no useful purpose would be served by a deputation waiting upon the Highbury Trustees .. that in view of the fact that a Pensions Hospital at Leicester is closing down, it is doubtful that Highbury will be vacated under a period of less than 5 or 6 years ...". (An ominous anticipation suggestion made was, that in the event of Highbury being obtained, for reasons of economy it would be necessary to close Woodlands and transfer the whole of the work to Highbury. I wonder what George Cadbury would have said to that?)

The City of Birmingham Council Health and Education Committees' were being requested to give full maintenance charges to the Woodlands and Forelands, particularly in relation to Tubercular bone disease patients. The response was that full cost of maintenance could not be recommended "... in any Hospital not under their full control ...".

With regard to the Education, the response was the same, but that the Council was approaching the Amalgamated Institutions with a view to a closer co-operation in the treatment of children throughout the City suffering Orthopaedic defects.

Developments elsewhere include, the fact that Vicarage Road, is now open. Half the beds occupied, the remainder will be fitted as soon as the Cooking Apparatus is completed. The Cripple's Union reports that work in connection with the electric lighting, at Woodlands, is practically completed, the English Electric Co. having presented the Cable free of charge.

The Hospitals and Clinics Sub-Committee is looking at the needs of establishing a workshop, as the boot department at Islington Row (Previously set up with high hopes) is totally inadequate. There is a need for alterations and repairs to be made for children attending the Massage Department, and additional workers are required. Work must be done on the Premises, and a kitchen at Broad Street, was to be set up as a boot-shop, with the following machinery:-

Finishing Machine-£55-10-0.	Last Stand- £2-0-0.	Motor-£16-10-0.
Polishing Machine-£15-0-0.	Anvil- £2-0-0.	Forge-£5-0-0.
Stitching Machine- £15-0-0.	Brazing Outfit-£2-0-0.	
Finishing Racks- £2-0-0.	Benching Timber-£5-0-0.	

Arthur Haigh, a pensioner, who had received training in the boot shop at Highbury, had been engaged on a month's trial at £2-10-0. pw. Four more lads, plus one for the Splint-work, to be employed.(Leonard Adams was appointed Splint Worker, on 22nd September 1925, at wages commencing 7/6d pw.)

With the old ticket system 'Drugs' had been supplied free of charge on the production of the ticket every six weeks. It is now recommended that a charge be made to cover the cost of the drugs and the Dispenser's salary. Necessitous cases free or reduced charge.

A Junior House Surgeon, Miss Evelyn Mag, aged 34 yrs, M.B., Ch.B.

B'ham.1924, took up her appointment in September 1925. The Medical Committee also recommended, that a small room at the Woodlands be fitted out as a Bacteriological and Clinical room, for the use of House Surgeons.

Mr Wilson Stuart and Mr. Leather are appointed as Extern Medical Officers at Smethwick and Nuneaton, respectively. A Scarletina out-break at the Forelands, prompted the call to Extern Clinics, that no patient should be admitted or transferred from one Institute to another without being examined by the Medical Officer of that Institute. Also it was suggested that a Small Isolation Block be provided at Forelands, together with a request that the dressings rooms be improved.

The proposed formal opening of Broad Street by the Amalgamated Hospital's President Lord Ednam, and the Lord Mayor, was to be the 3rd week of November 1925. The Medical Board was also laying out its views re facilities, rooms, equipment, even extensions, thus:- Purchase of Back-Premises at Broad Street. Facilities for the examination of 80 to 100 outpatients in one afternoon. The majority of patients should be undressed for proper examination; and stating the limitations of the existing Newhall Street site, there being only two screens available; the room is overcrowded with two nurses, the Secretary, the Surgeon and his Assistant. There are no facilities for the removal or application of Plasters, in or near the Consulting Room. The accommodation considered necessary being:- A large heated waiting room with lavatories, Male and Female; Two easily accessible examination rooms with 8 to 12 screened couches in each, subsequently agreed that there was no need to have couches in separate cubicles, and curtain screening advised. Greater privacy to be provided in Sister's room, a portion of each room being screened off for the removal and application of plasters. A fully equipped X-ray Department. Personnel requirements being; a Sister-in-Charge trained in plaster-work and in the measurement and application of splints. A Sister-in-Charge of the After-Care Department; an Almoner; an Instrument Maker; and a Surgical boot-maker readily available for consultation.

The Ladies of the Linen League have given £100 towards the purchase of blankets in addition to equipping Vicarage Road. The House Committee having completed the work assigned, viz., the installation of Central Heating, decorating and sundry repairs at Broad Street ask that they now be liberated from further responsibility. The work being taken over by the Hospital's and Clinic Sub-committee.

The period September 1925 to June 1926 saw a slight matter of disagreement with the immediate neighbours of the Vicarage Road Hospital. In an attempt to overcome a complaint re the 'noise' of the male patients, screens and curtains to deaden sound, and increased height of garden walls and additional fencing to prevent the mens' ward from being seen, and silencers in the lavatories, were proposed. After protracted discussions the neighbour eventually decided to sell his interest in his house, and the Amalgamated Hospital made an offer. Subsequently purchasing the property. The male patients, however, had been transferred to Newhall Street in February 1926.

Miss Cox, talking to the Workmen's Auxiliary Committee, (an offshoot of the Cripple's Union, details of which are given in Chapter 5). January 11th, 1926 reported the early success of the Amalgamation and proposed developments. The Orthopaedic Hospital and Vicarage Road would be eventually moved to the Woodlands, so making one large up-to-date Orthopaedic Hospital serving the whole of the Midlands. The outpatient departments of Newhall Street and Islington Row, and Office, moving to Broad Street. When completed there will be a minimum of 300 beds.

A month later Mr. H.F.Harvey reported, to the same group. There was an overdraft of £10,000 on the Bank, requiring continued money raising activities (a prime function of the W.A.C.). In line with the philosophy of the Cripples' Union thinking, he went on to say "... what a tragedy it was that on the waiting list were those who, if not attended to now, would grow up incurable, a burden to themselves, their friends and to the whole community..." Miss Cox then spoke highly of the harmony existing between the staffs of the Orthopaedic Hospital and the Cripples' Union.

The Woodlands House Committee reports in November 1925 'Fire Drill' arrangements, and at a cost of £7-12-0d the purchase of a Sewing Machine, for the Splint Room. The Hospital Saturday Fund contribution system is also affected by the abolition of the Note System, regarding the treatment of subscribers to that fund. The H.S.F suggesting that inpatient and outpatient treatment, including massage, and electrical treatment should be given, and in the case of boots, instruments etc., each case should be treated individually and if necessary application made to the H.S.F. for help towards the cost. The H.S.F. subsequently gave the Orthopaedic Hospital £275 in lieu of tickets, and a donation of £525, and the Cripple's Union a donation of £850.

Mrs George Cadbury together with the Architect to the Bournville Trust, proposed obtaining additional land at Woodlands, comprising some 41/2 acres adjoining Woodlands, on the Convent side with a frontage on Bristol Road.

The Forelands House Committee, have found the equipment (Batteries) for lighting inadequate "... Eleven Storage Batteries have been transferred from Woodlands replacing the worst cells ...". With a view to updating the, then, technology , the Matron "... has been requested to canvass the House-holders on Rock Hill with a view to ascertaining whether they will be prepared to take the electric light if the cable is laid up to the Rock.".

There are some difficulties being experienced in obtaining payments from patients for X-rays, due to them having to find further payments for, instruments, boots, and massage. The Committee therefore recommended that Radiographs should be supplied free of charge , except in very exceptional circumstances, or when paid for by outside funds or authorities.

Further, re the purchase of an additional 41/2 acres of land, the position, from the Bournville Trust regarding proposed future housing developments, is given in January 1926 "... as you know there is a road projected behind the Woodlands which runs from the Valley, North East into Hole Lane. A building depth from this Road would leave an area of land behind its back boundary and the back boundary of the Woodlands which the Village Trustees would be willing to sell ... providing that no buildings were to be put upon it. It was suggested that the line of the Wards should be moved a little distance towards Bristol Road, in order to leave as much space as possible between themselves and the houses to be built on the proposed road".

There is still 'Old Gas Lighting' at Newhall Street, "... Not only is the

Electric lighting grossly inadequate but that also the gas lighting in such an old building is dangerous ...". I was a little surprised to find the Woodlands House Committee statement that "... Pig Sties were erected and pigs purchased, in October 1924, and since then £50 profit had been made. There are still three pigs to be sold, value £27 and eight small pigs just purchased". And did you know? Stretchers were being purchased at 2/11d each, the Forelands did, they ordered 70.

Bogus Appeals are nothing new. The Citizen's Society having reported that a Society was carrying out a Campaign in Birmingham for raising funds on behalf of poor and crippled children. There was reason to suspect the genuine nature of the work.

The supporting of beds, at the Hospitals, was not only from individuals, but as this note indicates, even from private schools. Sadly it marks the end of that support, Miss Cull of Erdington having informed the Committee that owing to the closing of her School the Contributions in Supporting the 'Iona' bed will cease". Appreciation was expressed for the splendid work done and the raising of £364-14-9¹/₂d.

A Recommendation was made by the Woodlands Committee that a hut be provided at a cost of £275, with £140 for equipment, for the accommodation of 14 patients. Also that an open-air ward for accommodating 12 babies be provided at the Woodlands, in order that the existing babies ward can be used as a recovery ward. Following the retirement of Miss Margurite Cook, Miss Littlewood (from the Anstey Physical Training College) was appointed Head Masseuse and Teacher. 101 Newhall Street, the Nurses Home, is taking care of its Caretaker and House-keeper, Mrs. Dearman, who is in receipt of a wage of 7/8d weekly. Her husband is now drawing his old age pension 30/- in all. The Finance Committee recommended, that in view of Mrs. Dearman's efficient service her wages should be increased to 20/- weekly.

The Forelands was to appoint Miss Rayment as Sister-in-Charge, she working for the first three months at Woodlands, before taking up her duties. Sister Lamb being transferred from Woodlands temporarily to Forelands.

A letter had been received from the Charities Commission asking from what source the money was to be provided for the purchase of the additional land at Woodlands. Mrs George Cadbury stated that she will be pleased to purchase the Land from the Bournville Trust and present it to the Hospital.

The First Annual Report of the Amalgamated Institutions (to December 31st, 1925) spoke well of the success of the co-ordination and centralisation at Broad Street it having been in use as from 1st September, for Massage, Electrical and Remedial Exercises, under the control of Dr. S.A.MacPhee. The staff including a Head Masseuse with 16 Assistant Masseuse a complete department for treatment by artificial sunlight having been added, and saw the new outpatient department with its X-ray rooms, metal shop, leather shop and offices, as excellent facilities treating an average of 700 patients a week. Newhall Street had seen over the year 388 patients admitted, 600 operations performed and 3,300 outpatient attendances. Vicarage Road, with its extensions, had been fully utilised for the treatment of 'certain long-term' cases, no provision having been made previously. At the Woodlands the beds were fully occupied, mainly by children requiring prolonged treatment. 306 patients admitted, 217 operations and 304 discharged for further treatment at Forelands or the Central Clinic.

The Medical Report for 1926-7, announced the death of Dr. Macphee, and that in March 1927 New Buildings had been completed at Broad Street, occupation taking place the following month. Formally opened by The Rt. Hon. Neville Chamberlain. M.P. April 8th. The Birmingham Gazette kindly extended the usefulness of a Wireless installation, with a gift of 33 pairs of headphones.

Sir Gilbert Barling, who had ensured the successful amalgamation, and held the Office of Chairman for the first two years, had been, through severe illness, forced to resign his position. Sir James Curtiss becoming his successor.

The land given by Mrs George Cadbury, at the Woodlands, was now to be developed for extensions. To that end a public appeal had been made for £10,000 (to clear off debt), and £40,000 for the extensions in order that 'patients could be transferred from the old and unsuitable buildings in

Newhall Street (and from Vicarage Road)'. Additional beds being urgently needed with 500 cases on the waiting list.

Wednesday 2nd November 1927 found the Hospital sharing the Prince of Wales (Later Edward V111) during his visit to Birmingham, primarily to open the 'Birmingham-Wolverhampton New Road'. On his return journey to Birmingham, the Prince's reception took place at the Rednal Tram Terminus, (a landmark for generations of Brummies), entering the Lord Mayor's car, and on reaching the Crippled Children's Hospital (not yet thus named), made an unofficial visit. "The weather being dry, many of the little cripples were brought out, and while the more serious cases were wheeled out on their beds, others were lined up at the side of the road".

The Third Annual Report for the year ending 31st December 1927, opens with the Committee expressing its pleasure at the success of the public appeals for the building funds and debt extinction, The appeal outcome details are interesting, re the rapidity of its support and by two other sources of income stated. Launched in the Council Chamber of the Council House, by the Lord Mayor, and Lord Ednam, Hospital President, supported by the Principal of the University (Presumably, Grant Robertson). The day following "... the magnificent first list was published in the press amounting to over £13,000". In addition a large amount was raised as a result of an Air Pageant held at Castle Bromwich on July 4th "Started in a small way (see W.A.C. details) this had become a Civic function ... nothing comparable to the display having been seen outside Hendon", which raised £4,520-0s-10d. The Birmingham Rotary Club also made a magnificent donation of £755.

By the end of the year the Appeal Fund stood at - £31,658-6s-11d, £10,000 going to debt extinction, and together with the sale of the Newhall Street premises and land at Quinton (never used), the much needed extensions at Woodlands could be carried out.

Perhaps an even more immediate important event was the change of 'Title', (which was to carry the Hospital through for the next 21 years). The original 'unwieldy' amalgamation name having been agreed by the Hospital Committee "... to retain as far as possible associations with the past history of both hospitals". A petition to use the suggested title passed to the Home

Secretary, in early December, was followed on the 23rd December by a reply stating that "His Majesty the King (George V) had graciously approved the title 'The Royal Cripples Hospital, Birmingham', being bestowed on the Hospital as from January 1st. 1928".

Nevertheless, all subsequent Reports carried the Heading:

The Royal Cripples Hospital, Birmingham.

incorporating

The Birmingham Cripples Union

and

Royal Orthopaedic and Spinal Hospital.

and so, on to 1948 and the next upheaval, the NHS.

Rotary Wards
source: Royal Cripples Hospital Reports. 1925-29
photo: Brian Jones

Royal Orthopaedic & Spinal Hospital, Newhall Street
Source: Royal Cripples Hospital Reports 1925-28
photo: Brian Jones

Broad Street Clinic
where Out-Patient and Administrative work is being concentrated.
Source: Royal Cripples Hospital Reports 1925-28 photo: Brian Jones

Chapter 4

1928 to 1948
The Last Years of the Voluntary Institute.

The year 1928 saw the development of the scheme for providing orthopaedic treatment for Birmingham children in co-operation with the City Authorities. The Broad Street Outpatient Department having treated, 1,030 of Birmingham's children of school age, 3,994 attendances in the Outpatient Department and 11,629 attendances in the Massage Department. The Education Authority had agreed to the transfer of suitable cases to Remedial Clinics at Sheep Street and John Bright Street, to relieve pressure at Broad Street. The Board of Education had also recognised as 'school attendance' all children visiting the various Clinics.

The Woodlands School 'pleasantly records' that Miss King and two Assistant teachers, Miss Margerison and Miss Bull, have been with us from the start Medical and Surgical treatment has progressed, there now being 109 beds with an increase to 177 expected.

The next years report shows further progress, Newhall Street Hospital has closed, (it is ready to be pulled down), and the patients transferred to the Woodlands. The Committee gave their thanks to Miss Hadley and Sister Mountford who "remained to the very last". Miss Hadley immediately took up her duties as Matron at Hammerwich Hospital (near Lichfield), Sister Mountford moving with her. The property was sold for £2,750, and with the Outpatient Department in Great Charles Street having previously been sold for £4,750. a mortgage of £1,800 paid off, hopefully some £5,580 would go towards the Woodlands extensions.

With the retirement of Sir James Curtis K.B.E. the position of Chairman of the Royal Cripples Hospital was accepted by Mr. H.F.Harvey. The good news being tempered by the announcement of the impending resignation of Miss Christine Cox, the General Secretary, due to ill health.

In addition to the erection of 3 new wards, an operating block and Nurses Home, four existing wards were altered, kitchens enlarged and fitted with

91

'every modern convenience', and the electrical installation in the main building (the original 'Woodlands') completely overhauled. Other donations raised came from: Lady Davis and her enthusiastic Committee £1,388-11s-2d: Birmingham Rotary Club £804-4s-10d for the furnishing of new wards for boys and girls, known as the 'Rotary' Wards, and from a Woodlands Fete £468-1s-11d.

November, 1929 saw the opening of the New Wards, by Her Royal Highness the Duchess of York (now the Queen Mother) accompanied by the Duke of York, (later King George V1). The occasion marking some special donations from: Aston Chain and Hook employees £1,000 for a bed endowment; Sir W. Waters Butler and Mr. H. Butler £250 to go with their previous gift of £250 to the building fund, to name a bed in memory of their father and mother, William and Mary Butler. Further gifts throughout the year coming from: Birmingham Mail 'Xmas Tree Fund' £1,000, inclusive of £500 from the Birmingham and District Butchers' Trade and Benevolent Association: Anonymous gifts amounting to £1,600, and from the Workmen's Auxiliary Committee £500 towards cot endowment.

There is clearly a great swell of support being shown for the Hospital at this date. There is still some concern re the facilities for nurses, a call coming for a Recreation Hall. "...The Hospital is five miles from the centre of the city, and staff are therefore obliged to find their own amusements. Some relaxation in a nurse's strenuous life is essential".

The Forelands was to lose, in 1930, Miss Moore who had been Lady Superintendent since the opening in 1921. Miss A.K.Lamb, formerly Assistant Matron at Woodlands, was appointed Matron-in-Charge, and Miss Shaw appointed Head Mistress of the school.

Another stalwart, the Vice-Chairman (together with Mr. H.F.Harvey at the 1925 amalgamation) Mr. J.H.Francis O.B.E., J.P., announced his retirement, during 1930. he having been associated with the Royal Orthopaedic and Spinal Hospital, for 15 years. Resignations from the Management Committee also included Laurence Cadbury and Allan Tangye.

The staff recreation hall came through the kindness of Colonel and Mrs. A.J.Rabone "... a beautiful Hall has been built in memory of their son,

Captain Brian Rabone." The staff, then numbering 90. Improvements against inclement weather include the supply of Weather screens, for the adult wards, but "... in the first plan no provision made for the children's ward of 60 beds".(!). The statement continues; "It has been found that the rain and snow drive into these wards, and some protection is necessary..." (does this relate only to the adult wards, if not it appears to suggest some change in the open-air system)? Just as his predecessors (at Newhall Street) had, Mr. H.F.Harvey was quite happy to undertake the supervision of the lay-out of the grounds, working with Mr. J. Smith, Superintendent of the Parks Department, and Mr. J. Humphries of Edgbaston Botanical Gardens. Cutting across his grounds would have been "... a road across the field to the south of Woodlands be cut to provide direct access to the Nurses Home and Recreation Hall, at a cost of £275."

Open-air ward patients were soon to be pleased with the gifts of 'Hotlock' Food Wagons, from employees of the Birmingham Public Works Department "... enabling meals to be served hot ... even on the coldest day". Miss Christine Cox also handed over £25, which she had raised. The success of the first wagon was such that that donation together with "... a share of the Fete-funds ..." enabled the purchase of two more.

Belmont was opened on 16th September 1929, as a hostel for students taking the course of training in orthopaedic nursing and massage, it being attached to the Woodlands and under the supervision of the Matron. (Fanny Smith). *20 students were to be in residence for the greater part of the year, and accommodation was inadequate. Additional dormitories and a bathroom, for 7 students, were provided by altering and heating the out-buildings over the stables.

By a reciprocal arrangement students were to obtain experience in general, surgical and medical work at the Queen's Hospital (Bath Row, later known, to Brummies, as the Accident Hospital), their students receiving additional tuition in orthopaedics, working in our wards and attending lectures by our surgeons.

An interesting 'Minute entry' reads:- "... Miss Littlewood is asking for a supply of bones for students' use; those at present being used are needed by Woodlands nurses. The matter was left in the hands of the Chairman."

*The Belmont Committee, Mrs. G Kenrick, H.F.Harvey, F.Wilson Stuart and J. Weatherhead, in the Minute of April 4th 1929, recorded; 9 Bedrooms for Students and 1 for a Maid or Caretaker. Later it was minuted that the first nurses went into residence on 2nd November 1929.

The statistics for 1930, in addition to the usual; Operations at Woodlands - 694, show the work carried out by the visiting Dental - Surgeon; Extractions-349, Fillings-88, Scaling-14 Ag.No. Treatment-39, N20 Administrations 10.

During the year ending 31st December 1931, Mr. A.M.Hendry was appointed second clinical assistant to Mr. Dunn; Dr. Guy Dain the Hon. Medical Officer to the Woodlands from its opening in 1909, having reached the age limit for the Medical Staff was re-appointed for a further two years; Dr. E.T.Starkie, one of the House Surgeons having retired was succeeded by Dr. Basil Dain.

The Central Branch of Toc H, and the Women helpers of the Moseley Branch, were instrumental in providing transport for outpatients unable to travel by bus or train. April 14th 1931 marked the opening of the Brian Rabone Memorial Hall by Mrs. Rabone. A description of the facilities being; there are cloak-rooms, a well equipped kitchen with serving hatch to the hall, and a moveable platform. The Piano being another generous gift from Colonel and Mrs. Rabone. The Hall is for the sole use of the nursing and domestic staff. Badminton is played, dances and entertainments are held.

Talking of piano's. The Woodlands school also receives a new one, thanks to the Public Works Department whose "... Annual gift took the form of a piano for school use - nothing could have been more welcome, as the old piano had become unplayable." Patients also received a visit, at Christmas, from Messrs. Lewis's *Father Christmas, bringing a toy for every child, whilst the Birmingham Rotary Club sent "... representatives weighed down with presents" for the children in the Rotary Wards.

The Linen League are certainly a Hospital fixture, this year with Miss Barrow still at the head, Woodlands and Vicarage Road Hospitals received some 1,418 garments and other articles.

Forelands was having alterations and additions made during 1931 to enable the reception of more acute cases; two dressing rooms; concrete platforms in front of the wards; movable weather screens in front of the classrooms; accommodation for additional Nursing Staff.-

*There can be few children, in Birmingham, that have not visited Lewis's Father Christmas.

The teaching staff, other than the Head Teacher, had become non-resident. Miss Tennant was appointed Head Mistress in July following the resignation of Miss Shaw. The services of a gardening mistress were dispensed with due to there now being 'few patients allowed to garden'. Choral and dramatic societies having replaced the more strenuous recreations. The Forelands was not to be left out of the piano stakes 'the Rock Hill District Horticultural Society' having 'most kindly' purchased from the proceeds of the 1930 Flower Show, a piano for use in the Chapel and a Billiard table for the trainee's hut, whilst a refrigerator has been provided from the 'Woodlands Fete' funds.

Three further deaths are announced in 1932, Colonel A.J.Rabone, who in addition to having given the Recreation Hall, had been a Vice-President of the Hospital and a member of the Management Committee. Mrs. Howard Heaton who had held the Office of President of the Linen League for six years. Miss Christine Cox passed away after a long and painful illness "... a tragic coincidence that one who had given the best part of her working life to the efforts for the cure of deformity should herself have been struck down by a progressive crippling deformity ...".

The Medical Staff noted the resignation of House Surgeon, Dr. H. I. Maister, and welcomed his replacement Dr. H. J. Knight. The Annual Meeting produced a glowing testimony of the Woodlands, by its Principal speaker Sir George Newman. K.C.B., M.D., Chief Medical Officer, Ministry of Health. "... Sir George challenged anyone to make a tour of this 'hospital in a garden' and not be moved to further effort on its behalf ... that in his opinion the Institution was one of the most perfect examples to be found in the country or elsewhere, of the voluntary enterprise and the chivalry of individual service subsidised by public funds, the result being, not a Government department managed from Whitehall, but a triumphant achievement of the co-operation between voluntary and state action."

The year to March 1933, produced a marked decrease in the waiting list, only 134, a reduction of 180 this to some degree as a result of the reorganisation at Forelands. The Woodlands school, sadly recorded that Miss King, who had been Head Mistress from its opening in 1914, was to leave, however she was moving on to pastures new, having in February 1933 gone to Switzerland to assist voluntarily with the convalescent centre at Davos. Her successor being Miss Gurney, who had had considerable educational experience under the Birmingham Education Committee.

At a later stage in this history Miss P.M.Reed (Matron at Woodlands some 50 years later) speaks of the Hospital's Education being well ahead of its time'.

Miss King prior to her resignation (1933) gave the following account of the education then being given. Surely this epitomises Miss Reed's later remarks.

"B. M. aged eight transferred from another hospital, had had prolonged treatment for tubercular arm and foot and had never been to school. First started by learning the sounds of letters and by the end of nine months, when he left Woodlands, was able to read any junior reading book. During the time he was in hospital he was taught to write, finally working from composition cards and filling in missing words, and to do simple addition, subtraction and multiplication. Having only one hand to use he was particularly careful, and everything he did was a model of neatness. He worked an elaborate pattern in wools on a canvas pochette, and before discharge could make almost anything with a meccano set."

Miss Tennant the Head Mistress at Forelands, having been granted sick leave, was to have resigned early in 1933, but sadly passed away before that period expired. Miss Edwards, assistant mistress since 1931 was appointed her successor in May 1933.

An anonymous gift from two ladies was the presentation of two day rooms for adult patients, at Woodlands, these being built on to the adult 'warm wards', one upstairs for women, the downstairs opening out onto a concrete terrace with access to the garden, for men. This facility being intended for patients who, although well enough to be out of bed, are not fit for discharge to their homes. Another gift early in 1933 was that of the 'Covered way' from the Nurses Home to the main building, and to Rabone

Rabone Hall
photo: Brian Jones

Hot-lock for Dinner
Source: R.C.H. Reports 1930-34 photo: R.T.C.

The nurses Walk before the covered Way
Source: R.C.H. Annual Reports 1930-34
photo: Brian Jones

Nurse Mrs. Jean Stuart makes her way from the Nurses Home to
Ward 5. along the Covered Way. 1997
photo: Brian Jones

Day Room - Ward 9. 1940.
Source: R.T.C. photo: Brian Jones

Day Room - 1997
on left Mrs. Frances College of Worcester
on right Mrs. Elizabeth Field of Bristol Road, Edgbaston
photo: Brian Jones

Hall, presented by Mrs. E. Sheffield. 258 ft. in length it was to protect the nurses and save them the need to don mackintoshes in bad weather. "... care has been taken that the erection shall not obstruct the views from any of the wards, and constructed with a tinted glass roof and open sides it will add to the beauty of the grounds, particularly when time has allowed for the growth of rambler roses round the supporting pillars." (what about the thorns)?

The ninth Annual Report announces the death of Mrs. Sheffield, she having lived to inspect and approve the finished Covered Way. Another Obituary was that of Sir Robert Jones, Bart. the "Great Orthopaedic Surgeon." (The Agnes Hunt/Robert Jones/Naughton Dunn story is covered in Chapter 6). The Medical Staff loses Dr. Walter Jordan who had been with the Royal Orthopaedic and Spinal Hospital from 1899, working in the Newhall Street, Hospital, in those early days before National Health Insurance, as unofficial Medical Officer. His vacancy was filled by Dr. L. Kirkby Thomas who is a well known Birmingham Anaesthetist. Mr.T. S. Donovan was appointed in June 1933 Clinical Assistant to Mr. F. Wilson Stuart, House Surgeons, Dr.H. J. Knight and Dr. Basil Dain resigned being replaced by Dr. N. Matson and Dr. M. S. Holtzman. Dr. J. F. Brailsford, Hon. Radiologist, is congratulated on the publication of his book 'The Radiology of Bones and Joints'.

A new Head Gardener has been appointed. This follows on from an earlier consideration of the Garden Sub-committee, re the possibility of further utilising land adjoining the Hospital for the production of vegetables etc. At that time it was found that the, then, Head Gardener had so many other duties, viz., attending boilers, general repairs to buildings etc, but that he could only undertake additional work of this kind, if relieved of the garden.

"... so far as can be ascertained at present the arrangements are working most satisfactorily and are likely to result in a saving on the repairs account and the cultivation of a good deal of land with a corresponding increase in production. At the end of the year it was possible to report that all the vegetables required at Woodlands, with one exception, of potatoes, were being grown." (why no spuds)?

The Spring of 1934, saw the Committee and Staff "...spending a delightful afternoon..." planting an avenue of flowering trees along the upper drive leading to the Rabone Recreation Hall. "... in the course of time this avenue will materially add to the beauty of the Hospital grounds."

The Committee is considering the erection of additional wards for paying patients, there being "... a real demand for private ward accommodation among those unable to afford Nursing Home fees, or who can be treated more suitably under open-air hospital conditions, and now that the waiting list has been reduced to reasonable proportions it is thought that the requirements of these patients should receive attention. The Committee was most anxious to ensure that any such action would not prejudice the claims of the ordinary patient. Every effort being made to see that the maintenance of the private ward accommodation should not impose burden on Hospital funds, and it was hoped that if wards were built on the cubicle plan they could be used for private or ordinary patients as necessity arises."

Belmont had a full complement of students in Orthopaedic Nursing and Massage at the commencement of the new term with five students taking only the Massage course. The Appointments of students who had completed their training were given; Masseuse at County Council Clinic, Derby; Corbett Hospital, Stourbridge; Princess Elizabeth Hospital, Devonshire. Assistant Masseuse at Coventry Cripples Guild; and Kettering General Hospital. In addition one student had taken up private work and one was employed, part-time, at this Hospital. Following a comment upon the excellent opportunities available to Qualified Masseuse it was stated, that "According to the new ruling of the Chartered Society of Massage and Medical Gymnastics, students commencing training after September 1934 will be required to have previously obtained their school leaving or Matriculation certificate".

The Lease on the Vicarage Road Auxiliary Hospital was to expire in 1936, no decision was yet to be made as to whether accommodation would be required there two years hence. The Forelands is to lose its 'Convalescent School'. The Board of Education having approved the new title 'The Forelands Hospital School'.

In view of the experience gained (by Frank Mathews) in the early days of the Crippled Children's Union, it is somewhat surprising to find that in the early 1930's the groundwork is being covered again. 1932 had seen a meeting of "... various Organisations in the Midland area working on behalf of cripples ..." to consider Training and Employment problems. Two years later "... whilst the need for a training centre still seems open to discussion ... many cripples are unable to find work without assistance. For others who are too disabled for normal employment, supervision and provision is desirable". It was decided that as a first step we should endeavour to find the number of such cases in our own area. Whilst for Employment "... in preparation for an enquiry of this kind the Hospital (Woodlands!) has already prepared statistics ... allowing for those definitely approved for training at Broad Street or Forelands, there are about 70 cases between 16 and 30 years of age ... at present needing help in obtaining training, employment or work at home. ..." That the larger number could not be employed except at Home or in some Institution, prompted a call for some extension of the Hospital's handicraft department, additional workshops, or a residential settlement. Hospital Registers of such cases must be kept as complete as possible.

The Baguley Cot Committee in addition to completing a balance of £1,000 to endow their cot, also gave to the Hospital a 'Covered Way' running from Ward 3 to the Babies Ward, and met the cost of tiling the sluice room adjoining Ward 4.

New extensions are recorded at the Eleventh Annual Meeting, for the year ending 31st December, 1935. Sir Gilbert Barling, Bart. declaring them open on October 22nd. The 'Minute' extract continuing, "...The first private patient was admitted a week or so earlier and the private block has been in use ever since ... providing accommodation for 18 patients." The Lecture Hall, the gift of Dame Elizabeth Cadbury , and the House Surgeon's Residence presented by the Management and Employees of the Aston Chain and Hook Company, form other delightful and valuable additions. The Lecture Hall, with Dame Elizabeth Cadbury's approval could, in addition to its original purpose, be converted as occasion requires, into a Chapel.

Towards the end of 1936 the Forelands was to lose the Matron, Miss

Lamb, retiring to her new home in Devonshire, and Miss Edwards the Head Mistress also retired. Miss Pocock, Assistant Matron at Woodlands was appointed Matron and Miss Connell, a member of the Forelands Staff as Head Mistress.

The Medical Committee reported in 1937 that "... Information has been supplied to the Ministry of Health in connection with their enquiry as to possible hospital accommodation in a time of a national emergency. Whether the next statement is related I know not, " The new Mobile Shock-Proof X-ray Unit purchased for the Woodlands is a valuable acquisition and enables X-rays to be taken in wards, when necessary in complete safety". There is an Appeal for £40,000 for rebuilding and extensions. The following year 1938 crisis consultations were going on with tentative plans for evacuation if needed. Colonel and Mrs. J.L.Mellor of the Dower House, Lapworth offered to place a portion of their home as an Auxiliary Hospital, and Mr. and Mrs. W. Williams of Weatheroak Hall, offered to adapt part of their home, in the event of the necessity arising for children to be moved from Woodlands. Additional buildings at Forelands were also available.

Mrs Arthur Rabone died in 1938. With the move of Miss Gurney, by the Birmingham Education Authority to Head Mistress of a Birmingham Special School, Miss D.M.Morley, previously second mistress at an Orthopaedic School under the London County Council, was appointed Head Mistress at Woodlands, whilst a similar change was taking place at Forelands, with Miss I. Brown, previously a second mistress at the Stanmore Orthopaedic Hospital, Middlesex, replacing Miss Connell, following her resignation in July 1938 as Head Mistress.

The Medical Report for 1938 notes a number of changes. Pressure of other duties caused the resignation of the Anaesthetist Dr. L. Kirkby Thomas, Dr. E. Mary Forsyth and Dr. Janet R. Welsh had been added to the rota of Anaesthetists. Dr. A.. Dorman and Dr. A. M. Keith, House Surgeons had resigned, being replaced by Dr. G. B. O'Neil and Mr. C.S.Walker, the latter in turn being replaced early in 1939 by Mr.D. M. Keir.

The 1st September 1939 saw an evacuation, from Woodlands, of 42 children to Forelands, where the training department was temporarily closed to provide additional accommodation. A further 20 being sent to the Dower House, Lapworth. (the Lapworth Voluntary Aid detachment assisting). There remained only 56 inpatients at Woodlands, patients whose treatment was nearing completion being sent home. The Institution was amongst the earliest in the country to commence admitting patients again, the Ministry of Health's Local Group Officer allowing urgent cases to return as from the 12th September, a number of empty beds being reserved at the request of the Ministry.

Extensions, at Woodlands, already in the pipeline had gone ahead being well advanced as at 1st September, and in early 1940 the new X-ray Department and extension to the Massage Department, were opened, and the new Ward Block occupied in May 1940.

Sir Gilbert Barling had been elected President of the Hospital, at the Annual General Meeting (May 1939), following the resignation of the Right Honourable the Earl of Dudley. (who had succeeded Lord Ednam in 1932). Sadly within a short time of taking the Office Sir Gilbert Barling died. His Obituary naturally recognised his work re the amalgamation, as Independent Chairman of the Joint Negotiating Committee. It has of course, been referred to already in this history that back in 1875 'Gilbert Barling had been appointed an Assistant Surgeon to the, then, Orthopaedic Hospital'.

The year 1939 had marked the deaths of:- Mr.Naughton Dunn, Honorary Surgeon to the Hospital, he having served both the Cripple's Union and the Amalgamated Institution since 1913. (See Chapter 6 for further detail.) John Weatherhead after 17 years association with the Committee, (a Ward to be named in his memory). Howard Heaton, Chairman, and Hon. Sec. Clive Levi, Vice-Chairman both before and after (Joint) amalgamation, and Dr. J. C. Hollick a Visiting Medical Officer to the Dower House, Lapworth. Mr. F. G. Allan, Mr. A. M. Hendry and Mr. T. S. Donovan having given many years service as Clinical Assistants, were appointed Assistant Honorary Surgeons, and the Anaesthetist, Dr. J. A. Ainscow resigned. At the outbreak of war Dr. James Smellie, Hon. Physician was called up, Dr. A. V. Neale was acting as his deputy.

The Sixteenth Annual Report for the year 1940 announced the election of the Lord Mayor of Birmingham, Councillor T. B. Pritchett as President in succession to Sir Gilbert Barling, and on a sad note that 'Woodlands was damaged by enemy action' in the Autumn. This hides a sad incident as stated by Miss Fanny Smith in her Matron's Report, exact extracts from which follow:-

23rd November. Enemy Action.

At 1.45 a.m. a high explosive bomb hit the corner of the Administrative Block - damaging four wards, Miss Moiet's bedroom (Nurse Steinhausen and Nurse Ponder) the Teacher's Room, and Mattress Room, which were demolished. The bomb came through the roof and two bedrooms, to the Teacher's Room where Sister Galloway and Sister Daniels were having their night meal. ... They were found under the debris of the Mattress Room four hours later. A second bomb fell on the corner of the New Block and exploded near the bathroom. Most of the windows of the service block and side wards were blown out, and also some of the doors, and part of the Sheffield Covered Way. The patients who were in the side ward were not hurt, but one man had a slight cut on the forehead, and the beds were covered with glass. The patients were wonderfully brave, so many were helpless but none complained. The Sisters and Nurses worked hard to move the patients under cover of another ward. The Cooks made tea for everyone. The co-operation and help from everyone was marvellous.

Another high explosive bomb fell among the trees, and it was thought to be unexploded, so four wards were evacuated next morning ... One incendiary bomb fell between the Nurse's Home and the Rabone Hall and was immediately extinguished by Sister Hyden ... the rest of the nurses and maids were not told of the tragic circumstances until they were called the next morning.

... The telephone girls were very brave, they were in darkness and water was pouring down from the fractured pipes. The electric light was off for the remainder of the night but was connected the next day. The Telephone and Exchanges were off until the 27th, but one private line was intact. ... The gas was off for 8 days, the water for 9 days, the Corporation brought tanks and the Well was used by pumping, the water was pumped out for sanitary arrangements. Drinking water was fetched twice daily from

Middlepark Road by Mrs. Burton, from Barnt Green, who came daily and drove our lorry. The water and milk had to be boiled. The heating was off 10 days.

In a tribute to Sister Galloway (from Glasgow) and Sister Daniels, (from Streetly) the Matron explains that the former was the Night Superintendent, Sister Daniels (a Ward Sister, also at Lapworth) being a relief Night Sister, both valuable members of the staff, loved and appreciated by patients and staff alike. Both having joined the staff on May 1st, 1936.

Another feature of the war was the intake of Belgian patients (for whose care Matron Fanny Smith was later to receive special recognition) to Woodlands. At the request of the Ministry of Health, 40 Belgian civilian orthopaedic patients, who had been in a hospital at Ostend at the time of the German invasion of Belgium, were admitted. The Party, which consisted of 24 women and 16 men, was accompanied by the Directress (Matron) of the Ostend Hospital, three nurses and the wife of one of the patients. Despite language and other difficulties the strangers settled in happily and by the end of the year, 20 had sufficiently recovered to leave the Hospital for billets where, they are still watched by the Belgian Matron.

Matron's Report adds:-

Nine have been placed in homes in Northfield and Weoley Hill. All are very happy, and return often to Woodlands as they feel it is their home. Matron De Wolfe has visited all the friends who have taken them , and has been busy with attending to changing of addresses on Ration Books and Identity Cards.

At the end of this sixteenth report a call goes out from the Committee to Subscribers.(when was income tax at 10/- in the £)?

IMPORTANT

How to make £1 - 0 - 0

become £2 - 0 - 0

Sign a Deed of Covenant to pay your Subscription for a period of 7 years. With Income Tax at its present rate at 10/- in the £, your subscription is DOUBLED without extra cost to yourself.

In 1940 The Medical Committee reports the resignation of Mr. D. M. Keir as House Surgeon being succeeded by Mr. S. V. Leary and, later, Dr. Agnes Crozier. and again the following year the Visiting Dentist to Forelands is Mr. G. Amiss. Dr. Brailsford and Mr. F. G. Allan become respectively Chairman and Secretary. Also at the request of the Medical and Management Committees, the Central Medical War Committee approved the appointment of a third House Surgeon, Dr. A. G. M. Watt being given the post of Senior House Surgeon.

The Eighteenth Annual Report for the year ending 31st December 1942 updates the List of Institutions, bed complements and telephone numbers HOSPITAL.
The WOODLANDS, Northfield;
normal bed complement 244, 18 for private patients
Telephone Nos : PRIORY 1166, 1167, 1168.

MASSAGE STUDENTS HOSTEL.
BELMONT, NORTHFIELD

THE FORELANDS, BROMSGROVE, HOSPITAL SCHOOL.
normal bed complement 74. Telephone No: Bromsgrove 2130.

OUT-PATIENT DEPARTMENT AND OFFICES.
80 BROAD STREET, BIRMINGHAM 15,
Telephone Nos: MIDLAND 3804, 3805, 3806, 3807.
And the Matrons and other Administrators :

Matrons:	Miss F.R.Smith, Woodlands Hospital.
	Miss S.Pocock, Forelands Hospital School.
Accountant:	Miss P.Stobbs. F.L.A.A., A.H.A.
General Secretary:	Miss Irene Whittock., F.H.A
Assistant Secretary	Mr.D.J.Wheeler., A.H.A

The Foreword of the 1943 Annual Report speaks of the steady and increasing work, though developments and extensions were held up, new records had been set in terms of inpatients and outpatients, with expenditure reaching the £100,000 mark. In anticipation of the return of peace, the Management Committee in considering future policy had set up a 'Post-war Development Committee'. A second Operating Theatre was urgently needed "... to make the Woodlands adequate to its position as the Chief Orthopaedic Centre in Birmingham and the near Midlands".

The inadequacy of the Broad Street building is already giving concern for both Administrative and outpatient work, and the Committee is faced with, either decentralising the outpatient work, or providing an entirely new set of offices and clinic, the existing site admitting no extensions. Even at this time the fact that "... a comprehensive State Medical Service is on the horizon ..." clearly prevents any such moves.

The Medical Committee warmly announces well deserved honours being conferred on its members: Dr. Dain, Honorary Medical Officer to the Woodlands throughout its existence, elected Chairman of the Council of the British Medical Association and soon to receive the Honorary M.D., degree of Birmingham University: Dr. Brailsford, Honorary Radiologist and Chairman of the Medical Committee had been made a Founder Fellow of the International College of Surgeons to the Huntarian Professor for the second time - the first occasion such an honour having been conferred upon a Radiologist. Dr. J.M.Smellie, Honorary Physician on active service in the Far East having been awarded the O.B.E. (Military Division).

A unique ceremony took place at Woodlands on 24th January 1944, when Dame Elizabeth Cadbury unveiled a Memorial Tablet to the two Night Sisters who had lost their lives in the Air-raid of November 1940, and to the devotion of other members of the staff who, on that occasion of great danger "Thought not of their own safety, but only of the welfare of the patients there." A pleasant surprise awaited the Children at Forelands, when having sent cigarettes to some of the men in the Services on Empire Day, they received a reply from "Private W. H. now on foreign service, thanking them and adding, It may seem strange, but I was in Forelands myself five years ago".

An increase in patients, from 5,175 to 9,247, and of outpatients 72,736 to

126,153 in the 10 years 1934 - 44, was the measure of growth and commitment announced at the Twentieth Annual Report and in the last year additions and extensions to the Hospital had been, at Woodlands: Private Ward Block, Lecture Hall for Nurses, Maids Hostel, New Boiler House, Extensions to Adult Wards 6 and 7, Cadbury and Harvey Wards, Extension to Massage Department. and at Forelands, a New Wing to accommodate trainees and staff, and a playroom (cost met by special donations). Temporary Extensions included the erection of prefabricated huts at Woodlands, Belmont and Broad Street, in order to relieve the pressure in the Physiotherapy and Rehabilitation Departments.

The Medical Committee reported that after D-day a large number of Service casualties came into the Midland Region, and that medical Staff who were attached to other hospitals treating the acute cases had necessarily to curtail their work at the Royal Cripples Hospital. This had resulted in the cutting down of the number of operating sessions and a temporary closure of certain outside clinics.

During 1945 Dame Elizabeth Cadbury was assisting the Woodland's urgent need for additional staff accommodation, by inviting some nurses to sleep at the Manor House. Others were being housed in cubicles in the Administrative Block (which had been condemned), and others occupying a house, and flats, on the Bristol Road. It had been the intention of the Committee to extend the Nurses' Home and Maids' Hostel to provide 70 additional bedrooms, however the Ministry had authorised work on the Maids' Hostel only.

Forelands was also suffering from lack of accommodation for the required staff increase. To that end 'The Birches', a freehold property in New Road, Bromsgrove was purchased, as a residence for 15 nurses.

The gardens and grounds at Woodlands, Belmont and Forelands, are never far from the mind of Mr. H. F. Harvey, Chairman of the Management Committee as the following shows. Mr. Guise, the gardener at Belmont had been transferred to Forelands following the retirement of Mr. Weaver. Woodlands had taken on Mr. Simmons, an experienced gardener, with responsibility also for Belmont. Having taken a personal interest Mr. Harvey was in touch with the Head Gardeners, and a scheme envisaged at

Woodlands for the beautifying of the grounds by converting vegetable plots into lawns and flower beds, with at Forelands more land being put under vegetables with a view to supplying the needs of both Institutions. The Committee announced its appreciation to Mrs. E.S.Martineau for their kind gift of £100 to be spent on the gardens at Woodlands. The condition of the Upper Drive which provides direct approach to the Nurses' Home and Maids' Hostel, is giving concern, as it is also used by lorries delivering fuel to the Boiler House, it was decided to 'Concrete and Light' the Drive.

The war over, and the Hospital announces its affiliation with the Queen Elizabeth Hospital, and that student nurses taking their general training have the choice of proceeding to the Q.E. or to the Bristol Infirmary or to Wolverhampton General Hospital. In order to attract future nurses a demonstration of 'Nursing Training' was held at Woodlands on March 25th, 1946, some 450 girls from Birmingham and the Midlands toured the Hospital. The same year, saw the resignation of Dr. Smellie, Hon. Physician (following his appointment as Professor of Paediatrics at Birmingham University) and Mr. E. B. Alabaster, Visiting Ophthalmic Surgeon, being replaced respectively by Dr. A. V. Neale and Mr. A. A. Douglas.

Mr. H. F. Harvey in his 'Foreword' to the last Annual Report of the Royal Cripples Hospital 1947 looks with sadness and some foreboding at the pros and cons for the future:

The Voluntary Hospital System, which has served our people well, for many years, comes to an end on July 5th, next year when the Nations hospital service passes completely into the hands of the State. Certain advantages, particularly with regard to finance, for which the Government will assume complete responsibility, are obvious, but it will be a matter of gravest regret if the spirit of mutual helpfulness and human sympathy is lost. We do not know, however, that the individual control by existing Management Committees will largely pass out of the hands of those by whom it is now exercised. The hospitals will be linked together in large groups under one Management Committee and each Institution will be given a House Committee, responsible for day-to-day administration, with powers not yet defined, but which will certainly be limited.

Mr. Harvey then talks of the intended grouping with 11 others including Selly Oak, Accident Hospital, the City's Fever Hospitals and Maternity Hospitals, Canwell Hall Babies and three Institutions at Solihull. Arguments in favour include 3,000 beds, and the widening of differing functions, but regrets the loss of the intimate control and efficiency. Also that it would lead to delays and frustration, with proposals for re-development and re-equipment having to go from House Committee to the New Management Committee then to a Regional Board then to the Ministry. Mr. Harvey is outspoken as to the initial moves re staffing:-

One thing is crystal clear. At the outset, the transfer of the hospital services will not supply a single extra consultant, doctor, nurse or bed, and will not cancel out existing waiting lists, which in the case of the Royal Cripples Hospital, due largely to the hold-up of the war years, now total 800. Indeed there is the disturbing prospect of a greatly increased demand upon medical and hospital services, which there will be no possibility of meeting in existing circumstances. ... The best that can be said is that in this, as in many other voluntary hospitals, every effort is being made to maintain and increase efficiency, and we shall all, in so far as we are permitted, do what we can to contribute to the development of the complete and effective service, which is the object of the National Health Act to provide.

The Committee comments on the post-war developments, and notes the foundation of a Preliminary Training School, a scheme closely connected with the Matron, Fanny Smith, who saw its inauguration, before her retirement. They had been able, during 1947, to carry out building extensions and improvements at a total cost of over £23,000. £4,280 was received from the sale of the 'Birches' the staff hostel at Bromsgrove, which was replaced by the purchase of 'Rock House' adjoining Forelands. The extensions included a new storey on the Workshop Block at Broad Street. Authority had been obtained for alterations for a new Babies Ward at Forelands, to repair the Solaria and install a new heating system to serve all but the original wards, which had been overhauled in the recent past.

Named beds and bed endowments during 1947 had been made by: Birmingham and Midland Motor Omnibus Company Employees, British

Magic Society, Chadwick End Women's Institute, Chelston Social Committee, Fairfield House School, Selly Oak Bus and Tram Depot Employees and Snooker Tournament Committee. The Rocket Club named their eighth bed at Forelands on May 31st 1947 and named a ward of 11 beds in May 1948. (see further details of the Rocket Club in Chapter 5.). Birmingham and Midland Staff of Lloyds Banks named two beds in March 1948.

As the final curtain is about to fall on this Voluntary Hospital System, let us recall the philosophy of the Cripples Union, which is still shining through as this 'Case Study' shows:-

D. M. was admitted to Woodlands in 1935 at the age of three years, and before she was finally discharged from Forelands in May 1946 had spent 9 1/2 years in hospital, receiving all her education there. She suffers from Osteogeneses Imperfecta (breakable bones) and when the Surgeon saw her at the Outpatient Clinic in May 1947, she was walking in double callipers and he recorded "she should be taught something at home as she will never be able to use normal transport". It was thought that the patient might like to be placed on the register of the Handicraft Department for home employment, but this did not appeal to her. She was interested in clerical work and wanted to resume the community life among other young people which she had enjoyed for so many years. The aid of the Juvenile Employment Department of the Education Committee was sought and after a number of abortive efforts, both on behalf of the staff of that department and of the Almoners, a post as a telephonist near the patients home was secured, the employer kindly undertaking to modify the hours of duty and to arrange transport. Following a period of training at Woodlands she commenced work in February 1948, but after six weeks her employer regretfully terminated her engagement owing to staff re-organisation. The Almoners have not, however, given up hope of finding a permanent opening for the patient.

Now for a few facts relating to Miss Fanny Smith, the Matron who on retirement on 31st December 1947 (actually took retirement on September 1st, having been granted 3 months special leave, in order to visit the U.S.A.) had been with the Institutions for 44 years, she having ended that career with special recognition for her 2nd world war services to the Belgian Patients. A certificate from the Royal Orthopaedic and Spinal Hospital reads: "that Nurse Fanny Smith has been in this Hospital from April 18. 1903 to January 4. 1908. Her conduct has been Excellent."

Signed by Matron Margaret Nicholl, William Thomas, Chairman of the Medical Committee, and Howard Heaton, Chairman of the General Committee.

Another, dated August 1st, 1919, signed by Mr. J. Hall-Edwards:

"This is to certify that Fanny R. Smith, The Royal Orthopaedic and Spinal Hospital, Birmingham, has attended a course of lectures and demonstrations on the theory and practice of x-rays, and at the conclusion of the lectures she passed a very creditable examination".

September, October, November 1948 was surely a most exciting period for Fanny Smith, for on the 14th September she was informed:

" Charles Prince of Belgium, Regent of the Realm.

My greetings to all in the present and future. Wishing to give evidence of our gratitude to Matron Fanny R. Smith of British Nationality member of the staff of the Royal Cripples Hospital in Birmingham.

By the proposal of the Minister of Foreign Affairs we have edicted and edict, Article 1. The Golden Palms of the 'Order of the Crown' are confirmed to Matron F. R. Smith.

Article 2. She will be admitted in the Order from today.

Article 3. The Minister of Foreign Affairs entitles this function, will be in charge of this present act.

Given in Brussels the 14th of September 1948. Charles."

This was followed by:

Ministry of Foreign Affairs. Brussels 24 - 9 - 48.

Miss Smith

It has pleased His Royal Highness the Prince Regent to confer to you, by my proposition: 'The Golden Palms of the Order of the Crown'

Wishing you my deepest congratulations for this distinction, I have the Honour to join to it, 1. the badge related to it - 2. a copy of the Act as a proof - 3. a form which I beg you to fill in and send back.

Believe etc. for the Minister of Foreign Affairs.

E. Van. Der. Helst.

The Investiture took place on the 10th November 1948, in the Lord Mayors Parlour at the Council House, and a public presentation of 'Other Decorations' was arranged, through Dame Elizabeth Cadbury, at the Hospital, by the Consulat De Belgique, Birmingham.

Fanny Smith was succeeded as Matron by Miss Mountain who had taken up her duties on 1st September, 1947. Miss Mountain, after obtaining her Orthopaedic Nursing Certificate at Wingfield Morris Orthopaedic Hospital and the S.R.N. qualification at University College Hospital, had gained further experience at Oxford and Stanmore. She had joined the Territorial Army Nursing Service in 1939 and nursed in France, Egypt and Belguim until January 1946 when she returned to the University College, taking the post of Administrative Sister.

A most important aspect of hospital life, to date not mentioned in this history, is included as it relates primarily to the 1930/1940s period. Committee Minutes state that. The Rev. J. E. Crowle Ellis, who became Rector at Northfield in 1946, was subsequently appointed Honorary Chaplain to the Woodlands. Roman Catholic patients are visited by Father Cassidy and regular Free Services are held. Local Clergy also visit at Woodlands, the Rev. F. W. Shepherd and the Rev. M. Buckler were accepting responsibility for Services held there.

Further to this, Miss Joyce E. Clark of Northfield, has most kindly provided the following information. "My father Mr. F. G. Clark, was one of the people providing Sunday Services for years, in 8 wards each week, from before the war. ... In the early 1930s a Methodist Local Preacher named Lucock, was passing the Woodlands one Sunday and wondered if Services were held there for patients. On finding that no regular Services were held, he rallied other Methodist preachers and, with the co-operation of the Matron and staff, Services were conducted each Sunday in about 8 wards.

When Mr. Lucock left Birmingham, the work was carried on by Mr. Geoffrey Whetnall, and when he was called up, my late father, Fred Clark, took over. When he had to give up, a Mr. Sidney Dowrick continued the work.

The Services were very informal. First you located a piano and dragged it to a suitable place, then hymn books were found and distributed to those who wanted them. Many patients were then long-term so most welcomed a change of routine but some tried to ignore the proceedings. Patients were asked for their choice of hymn and a very simple service ensued. Speakers soon learned to cope against a back ground of noise from other wards - windows were open and often half the beds were outside. I recall talking to boys who were bunting each others beds while small children were playing on the floor below - a very good training.

When my father was arranging the service, he was there every week and I know patients appreciated the chats at the bedside and gained support from the brief addresses and prayers. This informal aspect was phased out when someone donated a radio system to the hospital. Using this apparatus, one service was relayed to all wards but the patients preferred the old system.

During the war it became impossible to 'man' the services locally and people were recruited from further afield. Mr. Fred Westbury and his wife, of the Northfield Methodists, did continue to conduct informal services in the boy's ward every Sunday, for many years."

Miss Clark also provided copies of letters sent from the Management Committee of the Royal Cripples Hospital, to her father during the mid 1940s expressing their appreciation of the 'voluntary services' all being epitomised by "... it is a great encouragement to those responsible for the Administration of the Hospital to know that they have associated with them so many men and women who are so concerned as they are for the welfare of patients and do so much to help them ...". (Not surprisingly this letter was signed by H. F. Harvey).

Joyce Clark also supplied a 'Plan of Services' for February 3rd to April 28th, listing the time of services, 10.30 am, the wards - Girl's Ward, Women's Ward's, 2, 7 and 9, Men's Ward, 8 and, to cover the 36 services, no

With Windows and verandahs to let in plenty of sunshine these new wards at the Royal Cripples Hospital Woodlands, Northfield were opened recently. 5th June 1940. photo: Birmingham Mail

Miss Fanny Smith
Source: Nurses League Newsletter, 1967
photo: Brian Jones

less than 72 'helpers', male and female, husband and wife.

The note at the bottom of the 'Plan', contains an interesting comment;

1. Will workers please meet in the front hall.

2. We are grateful to Mr. Wilson who takes the Boys Ward.

3. In future will preachers unable to take their appointments please let me know in time to make other arrangements , thereby saving disappointment in the Wards, as well as a useless journey for the pianists.

Finally, we enter the year 1947-1948 with the list of Medical Officers in place, to serve through the last year of this Voluntary Institute.

Hon. Consulting Surgeon: G. Percival Mills.

Hon. Surgeons: J. B. Leather; F. Wilson Stuart; F. G. Allan;

                  A. M. Hendry; T. S. Donovan.

Hon. Radiologist: J. F. Brailsford

Hon. Medical Officer to the Woodlands: H. Guy Dain.

Hon. Aural Surgeon: Wm. Stirk Adams.

Ophthalmic Surgeon; Alastair A. Douglas.

Dentist: G. Amiss.

Anaesthetists: Helen Scott Mason; E. Mary Forsyth; Janet R. Welsh,

also, Linen League: Hon. Treasurer: Miss Burrows.

The last entry for September 1947, will have given heart to the hospital Gardeners.

"It was reported that the second gardener at Woodlands had recently left, having secured a post at Messrs. Austin Works. Following this resignation the Head Gardener raised the question of the wages paid to gardeners, and indicated that he felt these to be low especially in relation to rates paid elsewhere, and particularly to those received by garden staffs at municipal hospitals. It was recommended that -

Mr. Simmons should receive an additional £1 per week, and Brown, now second gardener, an increase of 5/- per week.

Before moving on to the next 20 years of the Hospitals history, I will now go back, in Chapter 5, to look at a number of events, primarily related to the Cripples Union, which add so much to the overall history, but would have interrupted the general flow of the story so far given. In some instances these move outside of the actual history but relate to people who had given so much to the development of the Institutes.

Chapter 5

Sections

- The Workman's Auxiliary Committee

- The Woodlands, Purchase and Gift

- The Forelands

- The Rocket Club

- Frank Mathews 1922 - 1948

The Workman's Auxiliary Committee

With the rapid and successful growth of the Crippled Children's Union since its formation in 1899 came the urgent need for an increase in funds. Frank Mathews being fully immersed in the practical everyday work was looking for other areas for income, and realised that there was a great potential awaiting from within local industry, sister organisations and the general public. To this end a meeting was called on October 2nd, 1905, in the Hurst Street Mission Chapel to officially form a 'Workingmen's Committee'.

It had, however, been informally founded nine days earlier as is seen from the report given at the First Annual Report of the W. A. C. by its First (and its only one for nearly 50 years) Secretary, Mr. A.E. Wort.

" ... it will not be out of place to mention how it came into existence. On Saturday 23rd September 05, the following gentlemen were invited to the home of the General Secretary of the Union, i.e., Mr. Frank Mathews, Messrs. Hogg, Styles, Mellor, Grainger, Smallwood, Potter , Sutton and Wort. After a visit to the works of Messrs. Cadbury Bros. thoughtfully arranged by Mr. Mathews, tea was partaken of. A round table conference was then held, with our esteemed host in the chair. He gave us a brief history of the Union's work among our little unfortunate friends. Hoping that he would be able to interest those present so that they would form a nucleus for the formation of a committee to tap sources which he himself would otherwise be unable to do. I might say that with the exception of one, they were all Fathers of Cripples. Mr. Mathews suggested hiring a room at the Hurst Street Mission and asking for some of the parents to attend a meeting ... on 2nd October. ... 25 gentlemen responded to his invitation. ...".

At that meeting it was proposed and carried that the committee be called 'The Workman's' Auxiliary Committee of the Birmingham and District Crippled Children's Union with Messrs. Hogg, O. A. Smallwood and Albert E. Wort, appointed (for the first 3 months) Chairman, Honorary Treasurer and Secretary, respectively. Ways and Means were then considered for communications with P.S.A -

(Pleasant Sunday Afternoons) and Adult Bible Classes to induce their committees to invite visits to their classes to explain the work of the Union and to ask for them to take collections on its behalf. Also to hold Street collections in various districts of the City and to hold concerts, and to place Collecting Boxes in Business Premises. "Success attended our efforts, being able to get dates on 6 of their plans, which realised a Magnificent sum of £10-10-6. I ,(Mr. Wort), would here like to point out that the cash received did not represent by any means, all that was accomplished. A class of people had been reached that before knew practically nothing that was being done for these suffering little ones, and as the attendance at the classes was anything from 200 to 900 people, it shows that this is no mean way of advertising the work ... and further, that these visits and collections are becoming annual contributions in many cases".

Collecting Boxes were also to be an important feature, the Committee had already had nine dozen made, "... many to replace those now obsolete, more to find homes in new districts. Permission being given by the Birmingham Co-operative Association to place a box in each of their many stores, also the Stirchley and Ten Acres Co-op store. Boxes are now to be found in the following districts :- Acocks Green, Kings Norton, Harborne, Ladywood, Hockley, Handsworth, Perry Barr, Soho, Nechells, Saltley, Small Heath, Kings Heath, Moseley, Bloomsbury, Yardley etc. These boxes are collected by members of the Committee at intervals of 3 months, the Xmas quarter proving to be the most remunerative. They have realised the sum of £28-7-03/4. ... A Carol Party held in the Small Heath District on Xmas Eve realised the sum of £1-15-0. ... The next item to report, and not the least, is the Street Parades. Where should we hold one? What Band could we get to play for us and what would they charge? ... Saltley was the first District decided upon. The Midland Railway Band was approached ... they stated their fee was £3 but in consideration of the object of the Parade, they would return us £2-15-0. ... The line of route was submitted to the Chief Constable who replied that he had no objection. The Parade was held on June 17th, 06, and the magnificent sum of £8-15-6. was collected ".

The second parade, 2 months later, in the Vauxhall District was less (financially) successful. The (same) band being unable to accept less than the £3 fee this time, the collection was smaller and the route traversed had proved a very poor one. The balance being but £3-8-9. Fortunately, on the same afternoon, a Member of the Committee had visited a P. S. A. at Astbury Memorial Church, Handsworth, and taken a collection of £3. There are numerous future Parades, many clashing with other events, e.g. the Onion Fair, which, of course, had drawn families into the City, away from their home districts. However a Christmas Morning Football Match played on the Small Heath Ground realised the "wonderful sum" of £56.

The Financial Statement for the First year showed a return of £91-5-4.¹/₄. comprised of Collecting Boxes £28-7-0³/₄. P. S. A - £25-5-7. Street Parades £23-17-5. Donations £4-2-0. Collections - £3-6-3¹/₂, Carol Parties £4-17-0, and a Concert at Saltley £1-10-0.

The adjectives used by Mr. Wort were certainly intended to raise the spirits of the Committee members, Wonderful; Magnificent, and as in the next example, "...The phenomenal amount collected by Mr. Davis 19/6 will no doubt stand as a record for some time, and the excellent Bag 11/10¹/₂ by Miss Jones, go to show the capabilities of some of our workers".

A street parade obviously required a Banner, "... Messrs. Keen and Scott undertaking to provide the material and make a cover for it when not in use." The cost for 6; 4 and 3 inch letters being:

In Plain white letters 12/9; Plain Gold letters £1-5-6;

White Letters with Gold outline or shading £1-10-0, All Gold to be English Leaf. The latter was accepted. The order for the Banner having been placed, and to be used at the Nechell's Parade on July 14th 1907. Unfortunately, despite being a glorious summer day, and the Advent of the new Banner, the end balance was but £2-19-2. (Comment was made as to the Banner being too heavy for boys to carry. I wonder where that Banner is now)?.

The W.A.C. were soon supporting the Chadwick End Convalescent Home with a visit, "... how grateful we felt when we finally arrived at the Cottage (went by train), and could not help but feel inspired to go on with the work after the delightful way in which the children entertained ". On Monday December 9th, 1907 the Committee sent a letter of thanks to "... Mr. George Cadbury for his magnificent gift of the Woodlands...".

On May 11th, 1908 "... started to march, collecting as we went, from

Small Heath Station at 9.30 a.m., on Easter Monday morning, with our Banner to the front and martial strains of the Olton Brass Band, in the teeth of a blinding snow storm, towards the Birmingham Football Ground, (Muntz Street), when a very good match was played, amid snow and sunshine ... about £50 added to the funds ".

Albert Wort had used "... the City of Birmingham's Motto 'Forward',," at the end of all of his Reports, as a Rallying call. This continued throughout the years, with sometimes slight variations, 'Forward and again Forward'. His Oratory was certainly well thought out, as the following call, on Tuesday May 19th, 08, shows:- "... this means something more than figures, looked at from an economic point of view, it means the saving of twenty little lives, and who can tell what that may mean, perhaps the pillars of some home, or useful members of our Civic or National life, or at least Self-Respecting and Self-Supporting Citizens. Gentlemen do you not feel proud of being able to do a little to bringing about this Ideal, and in conclusion may our Motto for the coming year be 'Excelsior' ".

Following their first visit to the Woodlands Mr.Wort says -

"... After an inspection of this beautiful place, made possible through the generosity of that public spirited man Mr. George Cadbury, would there were more men in the land, who realised as he does the sacredness of wealth, that he is only a Steward to mete out wisely for the benefit of humanity that which has been given to him".

A New Cash Bag is in demand by Mid 1910. "... the one now in use having got too small for our requirements." And for the next Cripple's Saturday 1 gross of Collecting Boxes were ordered. £25 p.a., was to be earmarked to have a bed at the Woodlands, supported and named (with a Brass Plate), by the W.A.C. Early in 1913, the Committee is looking for ways of improving income from Concerts.

"... various suggestions were offered, among others, that we might have more seats at 1/6d, and that the people might be packed more closely together by the Stewards".

A proposal was also put forward regarding future parades, "... A discussion followed as to the frequent stops on the Parades, and the length of same, it was resolved that in future there would be three stops, of ten minutes duration each ... two at Public houses and one at a Coffee house." Another, more successful activity, in terms of effort and return, were Flower Shows, one such day realising £22-16-9 (including sale of Post Cards) from:- The Lamp Tavern: Country Girl; Station Hotel: Highgate Floral Society: White Hart: Booth Street Tavern: Rodney Inn: Highgate Tavern and Sydenham Hotel. At this time a Badge Secretary was appointed "... badges to be let out to members on the payment of sixpence, which sum should be refunded on members leaving the Committee, and returning the Badge."

Moving on to 1922, the W.A.C. was naturally concerned at the announcement of the resignation of their Founder Mr. Frank Mathews. They having received a minute to that effect, strangely referring to "... a member of the Committee...". they subsequently received a letter from Mr. Mathews thanking them for their kind gifts, and "... that he really needed nothing to remind him of the W.A.C. also the friendship he had from them, being deeply engraved upon his heart, and he wished them every success in their future efforts to help forward the great work among the crippled children of the City." July 1922 saw a most successful outcome from a 'Cripple's Saturday', amounting to - £1,019-5-2½.

The Workman's Auxiliary Committee were kept fully informed by Mr. H. F. Harvey of events leading up to the 1925 amalgamation. (Mr. Wort was however, in line with his Mentor, Frank Mathews, not in favour.) The work of the W.A.C. did not however abate, March 1926 saw them receiving thanks from the Chairman of the Amalgamated Institutions Finance Committee for a cheque of £750, and six months later "... income from the Flag Day had amounted to £1,250 of which £1,000 had already been paid to the Hospital ". (This meant that the W.A.C. had, over its first 20 years, given £23,221 to the Cripples Union).

Mr. Wort is seen to be quite humble, when he reported, in connection with the purchase of a Typewriter, authorised by the Committee, that he had forgotten a very important thing. He had no table for it.

The years 1925/26/27 saw Street Collections totalling - £3,698-4-10¾ and Donations from Flag Days £2,642-14-1½. In 1926 the W.A.C. was looking for Stewards for an Air Pageant at Castle Bromwich. In March 1931 they were obtaining estimates for one gross of Badges with the wording "Royal Cripples Hospital" round the border, and in the centre "W.A.C.". Official recognition of Mr. Wort's work came initially in May 1932, when the Hospital Management Committee were drawing up a list of nominations for Honorary Life Governors. Mr. Smallwood having already been nominated, another nomination was permitted "... thought it only right that if Mr. Wort was eligible, being a member of the Hospital Staff, to nominate him ... as he with Mr. Smallwood are the only two original members of the Committee ...". Mr. Wort was elected a Life Governor in June 1932.

In February 1935 the W.A.C., had a slight change in Title, it becoming "The Worker's Auxiliary Committee. ... Each member would then be permitted to bring along their wife or friend who no doubt help the Hospital considerably with the various efforts of raising money, as it was thought that if it had not been for the Ladies help they would not have been the success they had proved ". Mesdames Stocks and Bottely were the first to be elected to the Committee the following month, and 12 months later Miss Winnie Wort, Albert's daughter joined.

At the 33rd Annual Report of the Worker's Auxiliary Committee in 1938, Mr. Wort said "... The formation of our Committee has never become fossilised, if it had been the case it would have been dead long ago." He was then presented with a Westminster Chime Clock in appreciation of his 33 years service as Honorary Secretary of the Committee. The 34th Annual Report is, sadly, the last 'Fully reported' one, of the W.A.C., due to reduction of space throughout the war, being replaced by just a short paragraph. Even more noticeable is that Mr. A.E.Wort's name was no longer on the frontispiece list of each Annual Report as Collector.

Not undaunted, the Annual Cripple's Saturday on the 3rd June 1939 realised "... the 'splendid' sum of £1,391-10s-10d ... the collection in Bromsgrove held on 8th July 1939, a very wet, depressing day and the amount collected £23-11s-8d, speaks volumes for the willing helpers who braved the weather conditions". Sadly Mr. A.E.Wort offered no rallying call, there was to be no 'Forward' to be heard again from this 'magnificent' body of workers.

Before giving a profile of Mr. A.E.Wort, the man, there are just two statements worthy of comment. The first from Mr. H.F.Harvey, from the 'Forword' to the 23rd Annual Report of the Royal Cripples Hospital, in 1947. "...With the assumption of full financial responsibility by the State, the need of such agencies as the Birmingham Contributory Association and Hospital Saturday Fund, without which many of our Local Institutions would have been bankrupt, and, in the case of the Royal Cripples Hospital, of the Worker's Auxiliary Committee which in the 43 years of its operations has raised no less than £67,000, will pass". The second, this from A.E.Wort:

" Those responsible for the future of our Voluntary Hospitals are passing through a very critical period, if the Voluntary system was to collapse, the State would necessarily have to step in, the flow of voluntary contributions would be checked, endowments would be lost, the full cost would fall on the heavily burdened tax-payer. But we feel confident that the voluntary system will be saved. We have inherited it, it has been our peculiar pride, it is our duty to hand it on unimpaired."

'No' - this was not a statement made as the curtain was falling in 1948, but was his 'Prophecy' given in the 23rd Annual Report of the Crippled Children's Union on March 31st. 1922.

Albert E.Wort

At no time in the above history of the Worker's Auxiliary Committee, is there even a hint that Mr. Wort was himself crippled. As a child in the early 1880's he had fallen whilst climbing, breaking both legs and nothing could be done for him. Later paralysis set in, and he moved about in a wheel-chair or on special crutches, even travelling by tram, train or bus. At an early stage he was showing signs of the determination, courage and drive which was to dominate his life, a life of complete commitment to the Cripple's Union. Visits to the Woodlands, Forelands and the Chadwick End Convalescent Cottage, would indeed have been arduous tasks.

Albert subsequently set up as a Boot and Shoe Maker, in Ladywood, including the supply of boots for cripples. It is with regard to the work that he carried out, not only as Secretary (and a Founder member) of the W.A.C.

but also in his role as 'Collector' for 40 years, that he must surely be regarded as one of the foremost men of the movement. In his Collector's role (not previously mentioned) he visited every possible business property and factory in every street in and around the city centre, soliciting subscriptions and donations.

He was to be seen on Saturdays and Sundays conducting groups around the Woodlands, with a view to getting subscriptions, and was greatly loved by the children and respected by the Staff. He was continually, leading from the front, promoting and organising money raising events. Winnie Wort his daughter, now in her 91st year recalls visting the Woodlands with her father, and at one time whilst staying with the Caretaker, going down the lovely gardens and-orchards, and often meeting George and Elizabeth Cadbury, who always had for her, a friendly word.

Albert Wort kept a hand-written day-by-day account covering the period November 20th, 1911 to January 27th, 1912. a fascinating record of sustained effort.

November 20th 1911
Called on:-
Messrs. Lane and Sons, Brueton Street
Mr. Lane hopes to arrange a collection
in two or three weeks time.
Aston Chain and Hook Ltd.
Will endeavour to take collection
in December
F. J. Batchelor. received 4/4d.

November 21st, 1911

Inspector Pope. Snow Hill, Station
Unable to see him as he is working
nights this week
C. E. Adams. Icknield Street
was informed that they took
a collection last May.
Frank Baker. St. Pauls Square
Received permission to stand at
gate with collecting box.

January 8th, 1912.
The Artistic Engraving & Printing Co. Edmund Street.
Could not find them, made enquiries and found they had gone to Great Charles Street.

January 10th, 1912.
Messrs ____, Tenby Street.
gave us £2 on January 3rd, 1911, will not do anything for us again, asked a reason for this, and if he had anything against our Society, he replied by saying he would not discuss the matter.

January 17th, 1912.

Attended the Office.

Did not go out owing to heavy downfall of snow.

January 18th, 1912.

Ditto.

Traffic greatly impeded.

The weekly amounts collected in the 10 week period were:-

1911.	20th Nov. - 25th. Nov.	3 - 10 - 8³/₄
	27th Nov. - 2nd. Dec.	3 - 8 - 10
	4th Dec. - 9th. Dec.	5 - 11 - 8¹/₂
	11th Dec. - 16th. Dec.	5 - 4 - 0
	18th. Dec.- 23rd.Dec.	20 - 8 - 11¹/₂
	28th. Dec. - 30th. Dec.	1 - 18 - 10.
1912.	1st Jan. - 6th. Jan.	10 - 8 - 11
	8th. Jan. - 13th. Jan.	12 - 17 - 7
	15th. Jan. - 20th. Jan.	2 - 7 - 2¹/₂
	22nd. Jan. - 27th. Jan.	6 - 0 - 1¹/₂

The Wort family were all involved, as Winnie recalls collecting with her mother in the Bull Ring on Saturday Mornings, the money being put into a simple wooden framed canvas bag. Also, at Broad Street Hospital, where most of the workers were cripples, they made Collecting Cans on Saturday afternoons, and put labels on them. On one occasion when the Cripples Union Offices were at Daimler House, Paradise Street, her father slept in the office after a 'Cripples Saturday Collection' guarding the proceeds , there being no banking facilities on Saturday nights.

Mr. A. E. Wort was made an Honorary Life Governor, as a representative of the W.A.C. in 1947, later becoming a Life Governor in his own right. He expressed his thanks to the Committee for the financial arrangements made upon his retirement. The Committee had under consideration the provision of a Motor Propelled Chair. This however did not materialise, but Winnie Wort recalls many journeys, from their Kings Norton home to the Woodlands, with her father in his self - propelled wheel-chair, along Middleton Hall Road and Hole Lane, she adding the necessary push on inclines. Albert passed away in the Spring of 1949.

There are two letters from 1947 following Albert Wort's retirement, relating to his contribution to the Cripple's Union.

This from 'Ellen M. Gibson', dated June 4th, 1947.

Dear Mr. Wort

I have been wanting to write to you ever since I read of your retirement, in the Monthly Report ... these sad happenings have to be faced, but you can look back on many years of devoted service to the cause, and your life has been a great inspiration to me. I remember so well the beginning of your work for the Cripples, and I do not forget your dear wife's share in it. ... I remember the names of all the children and all the incidents connected with the work - and how greatly I have admired the sacrifices made by the Members of the 'W.A.C.' & 'The Women's Guild'! ... Well, I hope & trust you will now rest from your many years of loving service for the cause & enjoy the rest of your life in the peace & comfort you deserve.

The second letter from a Director of A. D.Wimbush & Son Ltd (Bakers Confectioners and Caterers) Small Heath, Birmingham. clearly echoes the great respect with which Albert Wort the 'Collector' was held by the city traders.

Dated 17 Jan. 1947.

Dear Mr. Wort

Your letter informing me of your retirement touches a very tender spot - Addison said re a friend:-

Of soul sincere,

In action faithful, and in honour clear

who broke no promise, served no private end

who gained no title, who lost no friend.

If I could add to this I should say 'Well done', friend Wort, as regards Charity the best was never good enough for you. I never think of Crippled kids but what I think of you. May your retirement be blessed with the golden sunshine it so highly deserves. Our support will always be maintained especially where the Cripples Hospital is concerned. Our usual Donation follows in the course of a few days. Again well done.

Yours very sincerely

E.J.O. Davis.

The Cripples Union and Hospital

owe much to the work of Mr. A.E.Wort.

I am greatly indebted to Winnie Wort and Kath. Watts for their kindness in giving access to so much of her father's original material, and for allowing me to use the above information.

It is with great sadness that since this MS went to the publisher Miss Winnie Wort passed away on 14th August 1997.

Thankfully Winnie had been given a copy of the sections relating to her father, her comment -

"At Last my father has received the recognition he so greatly deserved"

Speaks Volumes

Albert E. Wort
Source: Miss Winnie Wort

THE

COUNTY

EXERCISE
B O O K

**EIGHTY
PAGES.**

A.E. Wort's Collectors Diary - Front Cover
November 1911.
Source: Miss Winnie Wort photo: Brian Jones

The Woodlands, Purchase and Gift.

This Section gives the exact description of 'The Woodlands' as given in the 'Sale Catalogue of the Estate of John Abraham Esq. Deceased', which took place on Thursday, July 20th, 1899. at 'The Grand Hotel, Colmore Row, Birmingham'. Followed by probable reasons as to why George Cadbury chose to give the property to the Cripples Union.

A valuable Freehold Residential & Building Estate at Northfield, having a frontage to Bristol Road of about 432 yards. Comprising a most substantially-built and handsome, medium sized, Mansion House, known as "The Woodlands," *27 a. 2 r. 13 p. of Pleasure Grounds and Old Turf Land, and a highly valuable Building Estate of about 95 Acres, formerly known as "Middleton Hall Farm,"
" Hay Green Farm." & " The Hole Farm." *(acres, rods, perch)

'The Woodlands,' being Lot 8. With Lodge at Entrance Gates, excellent Stabling, Carriage Houses, Glass-houses, Pleasure Grounds, Lawns, Gardens, and Orchard, together with convenient Farm Buildings, five Fields of Old Turf Land and Fish Ponds.

Is most substantially built and has an exceedingly attractive classic elevation in Brick and Stucco, with Freestone Facings; it is placed well back from the road and protected by an Ornamental Fence Wall, and is approached by a Carriage Drive, belted by fine grown Flowering and other Shrubs of mature growth, and contains the following accommodation:-
On the Ground Floor - Approached by a Flight of Steps, imposing Portico Entrance, Spacious Hall; Dining Room, 30ft. by 18ft.; Drawing Room, 29ft. 6ins. by 18ft. ; Boudoir; Library, 19ft. by 16ft.; Morning Room, 24ft. by 15ft. ; and handsome Inner or Staircase. Hall.   The Domestic portion, well screened from the Reception Rooms, includes ;- Servant's Hall, 18ft. by 14ft. ; Cooking Kitchen. 18ft. by 15ft. ; Housekeeper's Room, 17ft. by 11ft. ; large Butler's Pantry ; Cook's and Store Pantries ; Scullery ; and Back Staircase.

In the Half-Basement Story are:- Laundry, 29ft. 6ins. by 17ft. 6ins.; Wine, Ale, and Store Cellars, Larder, Dairy, Wash-house, Heating Chamber, W.C., and Ash Place; an approach to this Floor being arranged from the Ground level from the Yard.

On the Chamber Floor: Spacious Landing and Corridors, eleven excellent bedrooms, Dressing Room, Two Bath Rooms, Two W.C.'s, Linen Closet, Housemaid's Closet and Back Stairs, a Well-lighted Billiard Room, 24ft. by 18ft.; and on the Second Floor a large Attic.

In an enclosed Paved Court-Yard, are well arranged Stable Buildings, consisting of :- Two Stables of three Stalls each, two Loose Boxes, Saddle Room (with Stores over), two Carriage Houses (with Men's Living Rooms over), and an extensive Range of Lofts, in three divisions.

The Other Outbuildings include:- Fowl-house, Piggeries, Fowl-pens (with netted runs), Boiler Shed, two Coal Sheds, Brick-built Pump and Engine House, (with Deep Well), two Potting houses, and Open Timber Shedding.

The Glass-Houses, which have been ornamentally constructed in a first-class manner on the most approved modern principles, comprise Conservatory, 28ft. by 14ft.; Plant House, 26ft. by 12ft.; Stove House, 22ft. 6ins. by 20ft.; two Vineries, 56ft. by 20ft.; and Forcing House, all heated by Hot Water Apparatus from one Boiler; Cold Frames, etc.

The Farmery, consists of a substantial, recently-erected modern range of Farm Buildings, comprising Four-stall Stable and Loose Box, with Loft over, Harness Room (with Grate, Furnace, and Sink).and an Open Tiled Roof Cart Shed.

A Timber-built erection, comprising Cow-house, with standing for five Cows, having Loft over; large Pigsty, with Loft over; Cowhouse, with standing for eight Cows, having Feeding Passage behind Stalls; Chaff-cutting House, and Open Feeding Pens.

I am most grateful to Mr. Ivor G. H. Cooke of Hole Lane, Northfield, for access to the Sale Catalogue. His grandparents who in 1899 were 'sitting tenants' at 'The David's Cottage' bid for and obtained 2 paddocks, which backed on to the Woodlands.

There are numerous statements as to the acreage purchased by George Cadbury, but by identifying (on the sale plan) the most likely areas; The

House; Buildings; Lawns; Yard, (3.144 acres), Garden (0.457 acres), and Kitchen Garden, (0.806 acres) it would make it -

- 4.407 acres. .

The reasons for George Cadbury purchasing the Woodlands (George and Elizabeth had moved into the Manor House, opposite, in 1891) are not clear. An article in the * 'The Carillon', Bournville News, Autumn 1986 , by the late Mr. Donald Harvey, (kindly unearthed by Mrs. Moira Wright), entitled 'The Woodlands Connection' , states -

"... it appears it was for accommodation of senior staff and their families, from the Cadbury works ..." Combining additional information re-a Mr. Thackray, from *that source, with that from:- the 'Bournville Works Magazines' dated January, 1908 and June, 1916, (kindly provided by Helen M. Davies, Archivist, Library and Archives Department, Cadbury Ltd. Bournville), it transpires that:-

Mr. Edward S. Thackray (who had been with the firm since 1876, when it was at Bridge Street), was in residence, he however found the house too large for his needs, (there were, as seen above, about 40 rooms , including 11 bedrooms, in the House alone), and the journey to the works was not convenient. No other staff are mentioned.

It is fact that the first information given as to the offer of the Woodlands appears (in the Crippled Children's Union minutes), on November 14th, 1907. "... it has been Communicated to this Union that the Woodlands, Kings Norton(?) would be offered for their Convalescent Work, if the offer was likely to be accepted ". Eight days later a letter is sent to 'George Cadbury Esq. Northfield':-

"... On behalf of the Committee of the Crippled Children's Union I am requested to tender their most sincere thanks for your generous offer to present to the Society the property known as the 'Woodlands' situate on the Bristol Road, Northfield, to be used for the purpose of a Convalescent Home ..." signed by Montgomery Hooper - Chairman   Frank Mathews - Secretary; and Mr. T.R.Bayliss - Treasurer.

A second question begs a response. Why did George Cadbury give the Woodlands to the Union? Various sources enable the answer to be sifted thus:-   George Cadbury was one of the Union's Vice-Presidents, and

Elizabeth was fully involved with all of his activities, particularly in inviting the Crippled Children's Union to bring out, Annually, to the Manor Farm "*... some of the little patients, 150 at a time, that they might lie on the grass and revel in country sights and sounds for a few hours. George Cadbury had longed to do more for them ..." *Elizabeth Cadbury 1858 - 1951, by Richenda Scott. Frank Mathews was organiser of those visits, and he would certainly have made a great impression on George Cadbury. Added to that George would have been fully aware of the Union's need for a larger Convalescent home, the Chadwick End cottage being inadequate, and the financial position of the Cripples Union was insufficient to go forward with plans for a New Home at Chadwick End, at that time in the pipe- line. The 'Woodlands' was a perfect solution.

George Cadbury
Source: R.O.H. photo: Brian Jones

Mrs. George Cadbury
Source: Souvenir Programme 1929, Opening of New Buildings photo: Brian Jones

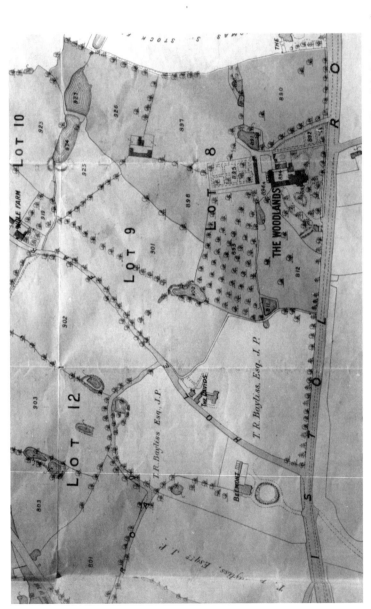

Extract from the 1899 Sale Catalogue of the Woodlands Estate showing 'The Woodlands', 'Belmont', 'The Davids', 'Hole Lane', 'Hole Farm'

Source: by kind permission of Mr. Ivor G. H. Cooke photo: Brian Jones

The Woodlands 1899.
Source: 1899 Sale Catalogue, by kind permission of
Mr. Ivor G.H. Cooke photo: Brian Jones

The Woodlands, Carriage Drive. 1899
Source: Sale Catalogue, by kind permission of Mr. Ivor G. H. Cooke
photo: Brian Jones

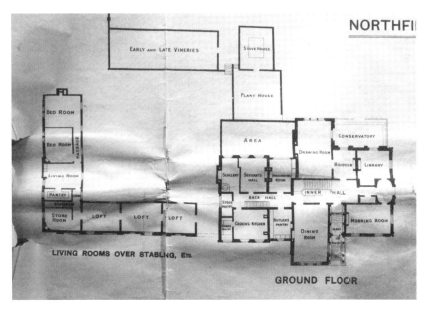

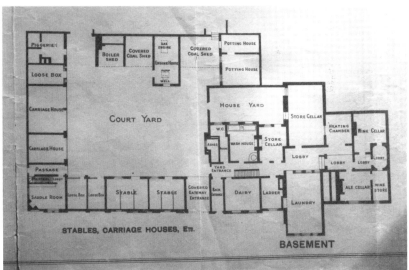

The Woodlands 1899
Ground Floor and Basement plans
Source: Sale Catalogue, by kind permission of Mr. Ivor G.H. Cooke
photo: Brian Jones

The Woodlands 1899, Main Staircase
Upper: 1899
Lower: 1997
Source: upper, by kind permission of Mr. Ivor G. H. Cooke
photos: Brian Jones

The Forelands

For 65 years the Forelands played the prominent role in the treatment, initially, of children from the Woodlands suffering Tubercular Bone Disease. All of the information gleaned for this history, whether from committee minutes, hospital staff, or personal experiences, speaks of 'The Forelands' in glowing terms.

The following information is extracted from the actual 'Sale Catalogue' for the * 'Forelands Estate, Bromsgrove', the Auction for which took place on Thursday, September 25th, 1919, held, as was that for the Woodlands 20 years (and 2 months before), at the Grand Hotel, Colmore Row, Birmingham. *ROH. archives.

The Forelands had been planned and built in 1874 by (the late) Mr. Charles Steer, who occupied it for a few years, and for ten years it had been leased to Sir John T. Middlemore.

Particulars

Lot 1. A Delightfully - Situated Freehold Residential Estate, comprising: 'The Attractively Designed and Well - Planned Modern Country Residence known as 'Forelands,' 375 feet above sea level, having a south-west aspect and commanding magnificent views, (including the Malvern Hills) .with:

Entrance Lodge and Cottage,

Well-laid-out Grounds, Park-like Pasture Land,

A Capital Farmhouse and Buildings (Forelands Farm)

total area 52a. 2r. 28p.

The Residence being substantially built with red brick, with stone dressings and stone mullioned windows, with slated roofs, approached from the main Worcester Road (1 mile south of Bromsgrove) by a long Carriage Drive.

Accommodation, on the Ground Floor:-Vestibule, Entrance Hall, Cloak Room (fitted with two lavatory basins and w.c.).

Palatial Reception Hall, 55ft. long, with two fireplaces, and door giving access to a Verandah on the south-west front.

An elegant Drawing Room, 25ft by 17ft., with a large bay window, and having a richly modelled frieze ; Garden, Entrance Lobby, opening out of Drawing Room and giving access to the Billiard Room, 28ft. by 20ft., with bay windows and ingle fireplace: A finely - proportioned Dining Room, 27ft. by 18ft., with large circular window extra, and panelled dado; Morning Room, 15ft. 6 ins. by 13ft. 6 ins.

On the First Floor approached by a handsome and easy staircase, is a Spacious and well-lighted Landing, with fireplace and two hot water radiators, around which are Seven Bedrooms and Two Dressing Rooms. Off the Main Landing are 'Three other Bedrooms or Nurseries'.

The Second Floor has five excellent Servants' Apartments, large Box or Work Room, Housemaid's Cupboard, Linen Closet, Bath Room and w.c. The Domestic Offices comprise Servery, with glazed front China Cupboards, Drawers, etc., and sink ; Store Room ; well-fitted Butler's Pantry, with large Plate Safe; Servant's Hall ; Cooking Kitchen with 5ft. Eagle range, cupboards and two sinks (h., c. and soft water), large Tradesman's Hall, two excellent Larders and w.c. There are also a large Cellar and Wine Cellar, and Heating Chamber, with 'Ideal' boiler.

A Lift runs from the Second Floor to the Basement. Opening on to the Servants' Yard are Coal and Wood House, Knife and Boot House, and a large Cycle House. Stabling accommodation is conveniently arranged around a paved yard, comprising Fodder Store, well-fitted Stable with two Loose Boxes and three Stalls ; Harness Room, large Carriage House or Garage with covered washing place.

The Engine House, with a 'Well' underneath, contains a 15 h.p. 'Crossley' O. E. Type Gas Engine, Electric Dynamo, hard and soft water pumps, a large rain-water tank under the Stable yard, Battery Room and Workshop adjoining, and two w.c's.

Lighting throughout by *Electricity, central heating, water supply, and a modern Drainage System are highlighted.

*this does not appear to be the full story as Matron (as has already been stated in this history) was canvassing in Rock Hill for support for cable laying.

The Entrance Lodge, (which was certainly lived in by members of the

Woodlands Staff, at a later date), is of modern brick and tile construction, finished with tile hanging and rough cast, and contains Entrance Lobby, Sitting Room, Kitchen, Pantry, Scullery with Sink, and three good bedrooms. Outside are Coal House and w.c.

A Model Laundry adjoins, with large copper, two glazed stone-ware washing troughs (h. and c. water), ironing tables and cupboards. The Cottage adjoins the Entrance Lodge, frontage to the Worcester Road. The Grounds, contain Tennis and Croquet Lawns, extensive and productive Vegetable Garden, well-grown fruit trees ; Potting and Tool Shed, Fruit Room, Tomato and Cucumber Houses.

These extracts will certainly bring back many memories of the Forelands House and facilities. Certainly the occupation of the Lodge and Cottage by the Head and Assistant Gardeners, and the use of the 'Large Dining Room' by staff and patients alike, has been referred to in the foregoing history.

The closure in the late 1980s of the Forelands and the subsequent demolishing of this House of such character was, to say the least, a tragedy. Today (1997) a most pleasantly laid out Housing Estate enjoys those 'commanding magnificent views' from Rock Hill. Sadly only the plaques on two entrance pillars 'The Forelands. A Development by Bryant Homes 1993', are left to mark the site of the Forelands Hospital.

The Forelands 1919
Source: Sale Catalogue, 1919 - R.T.C.
photo: Brian Jones

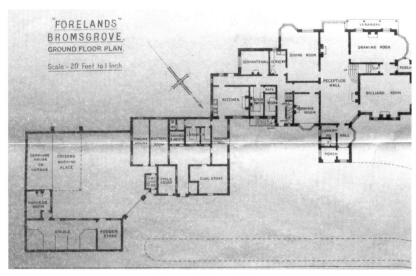

Ground Floor Plan
Source: Sale Catalogue 1919. R.T.C. photo: Brian Jones

Forelands and Lodge
Source: Sale Catalogue, 1919. R.T.C.
photo: Brian Jones

Forelands - Rock Hill. 1997
photos: Brian Jones

The Rocket Club

NON NOBIS SOLUM

'Not For Ourselves Alone' is the fitting Motto for the Rocket Club, which will be celebrating its Centenary on October 21st, 1997. That places them as having been founded, more or less, at the same time as the Cripple's Union, and that connection was, from the very outset, to be of great importance to the crippled children of the city.

Two of the early sections of this Chapter, have a direct relationship with the Rocket Club. Albert Wort was one of their Honorary members. (The basic history of the Club having been gleaned from Mr. Wort's personal copy of their Book, 'The Rocket Club, by Olly Hill and Mickie Fraser [being the history of a unique Birmingham Institution] published April 1949). The second being the Forelands to which they were to give so much practical support.

The Club was formed by 'Old Boys of Camphill and other King Edward the Sixth Foundation schools,' who gathered on Saturdays (P.S.N. Pleasant Saturday Night) at the Golden Lion, Solihull. Subsequent moves to the Woolpack, (Moor Street), back to Solihull (the Wagon and Horses), to the Exchange Restaurant in Stephenson Place, and the White Horse, Congreve Street, followed.

The 'Rite of Rocketry', (and their Rocket Symbol), "... the club's spectacular display of enthusiasm and appreciation..." originated from "... a member returning from a Scarborough holiday giving a demonstration, with actions, of how the Scarborough Rockets went up, burst and spread their beauty..."

The Rocket Club in the early days were very much involved in theatre visits, during which there was a custom of giving gifts to the Professional Performers and theatre staffs. Subsequently their habit of putting on home grown entertainments at their own events, developed into visits by the 'Stars' themselves. George Mozart and Nat Clifford being the first of literally hundreds of Music-Hall and theatre artistes to entertain the Rocket Club.

The contribution of the Birmingham Theatres with the Crippled Children's Union virtually from its foundation, with men such as Leon and later Derek Salberg (Alexandra Theatre) and the Rodway Family (The Old Prince of Wales and the Theatre Royal), and the Rocket club explains fully the reason for the subsequent benevolence of the latter to those same needs. The Rocket Club History goes on to say:-

"Charity was only casually a plank in the Rocket policy for some years. The club's first organised effort for charity did not come until December, 1914, when the catastrophe of war was turning the thoughts of all such societies to the duty of helping those distressed and bereaved. This effort was a concert at the Temperance Hall (Corporation Street) and was for the 'Prince of Wales' War Relief Fund ... since when many thousands of pounds have been collected and disbursed, that institutions concerning themselves with the welfare of children have long held a firm place in Rocket sympathy, and that no president ever vainly asked his members to put their hands down in a collective effort."

"During the presidency of Mr. S.W.B.Stephen, 1920/21. 21/22. 22/23. the club's interest in the Welfare of the Cripple's Hospital, and, especially of its branch at Forelands, Bromsgrove, crystallized into a determination to establish some lasting link with the magnificent remedial work being carried out. So began the effort to raise £500 for the naming of the first Rocket Club bed at Forelands. The scheme came to fruition in May, 1922, when the club's first official annual visit took place. ... Forelands day has since become a red-letter day in the lives of Rockets, who go to Bromsgrove to give the kiddies a few happy hours, and invariably have even happier one themselves! The firm of Wilder, some member of which has long figured as a vice-president, provides a notable display of day-light fireworks. Balloons are released, Clowns, conjurers and other entertainers join the fray."

"You'd think the atmosphere of Forelands would be charged with gloom. Not a bit of it. This is a place of hope and happiness. We who regularly take part in the Forelands Day may see sights that bring tears to the eye and a lump into the throat. We may find it hard to respond to the bright cheerfulness of the little folk who greet us so self-consciously. We may hurry away from some beds to avoid showing how sentimental we are."

A second Rocket bed was dedicated at Forelands in 1924/25, a third in 1930, followed by a fourth, and in 1932/33 a fifth, named after the then president Bert Browne, and a sixth in memory of Harry Butler. A seventh bed was named following the death of Leon Salberg, and with the passing of Bert Browne in 1942 a memorial tablet was placed on the Bert Browne bed at Forelands, and a handsome donation made to the Royal Cripples Hospital. "... whose claim on our generosity had steadily been recognised since the day, when Bert Browne handed over to our good friend Mr. A. E. Wort, the club's first gift of a few shillings." In their Golden Jubilee year following the death of their president 'Buster Russell' £1,000 was raised, of which £300 went to completing the purchase of the eighth named bed.

"...The climax of all that is best in Rocketry, was reached on May 29th, 1948. (less than 6 weeks before the N. H. S. take over), ... the cherished plan for linking the club's name to the Royal Cripples Hospital with unshakeable security by naming a Rocket Club Ward at Forelands."

"... It is worth noting that our first gift to the Cripple's Hospital was 13/- in 1913, long before Forelands was established, ... in 1914 the donation rose by one shilling and in 1915 it was one whole guinea. The first large gift £221-10-6d, was raised (all expenses being paid by members) at an Alexandra Theatre concert in December 1920. ... all told.... the club has contributed more than £4,200 direct to the funds of the institution ..."

The question foremost in my mind on researching this information was: Why was Forelands chosen for this wonderful generosity? Leafing through the 'Roll of Chairmen at Rocket Club Concerts, 1897 - 1948 I found the name H. F. Harvey. Need I search further?

In making my acknowledgments for source material I am greatly indebted to Winnie Wort for access to her father's copy of the 'Rocket Book,' and also to Mr. Sidney Caro, M.B.E. Vice-President, and Trevor Hancock, Honorary Secretary of the Rocket Club, for so kindly inviting me to a Rocket Club Dinner and entertainment. For me, it was a great privilege to have taken part in the 'Rocket Rite'.

The invitation to that dinner carried the statement -

" Throughout this century the Club has continued, in good times and bad, to uphold its traditions and still provides for those less fortunate members of society through its charitable donations ..."

Congratulations to the Rocket Club in this your Centenary Year.

Frank Mathews
1922 - 1948

My request, through an article in the Birmingham Mail, for information about Mr. Frank Mathews, following his resignation from being General Secretary of the Cripple's Union in 1922, resulted in a wealth of information. Although the overall information lies outside that of the hospital history, I am sure that in view of the Frank Mathews connection, it will be of interest, and does of course highlight another 'Movement' running parallel to our Institutions providing urgent care for, in this case, Invalid and Nervous children, the seed of which had grown in Frank's mind whilst developing the Cripple's Union.

Miss J. Jennings, from Edgbaston, starts the ball rolling:-

My own contact with Frank Mathews in 1942, was through the Birmingham Society for the Care of Invalid and Nervous Children. At the age of 12 I was boarded out at a farm near Ludlow. I did eventually lose contact with the Society round about 1947/48 although I had an occasional letter from Mrs. Hilda Rees, assistant to Frank Mathews, who continued to run the Society. (Frank Mathews died in 1948.) His widow, Evelyn Mathews lived to the age of 91 years, dying in 1968.

With reference to other convalescent homes Miss Jennings does refer to a Bodenham Manor School, Herefordshire, and Haseley Hall, Warwickshire.

Mrs. June Clark, Harborne, expands on this:-

I worked for Mr. Frank Mathews during my 'teens (I am now 68). He ran the 'Invalid and Nervous Children's Society' from two rooms in the private home of Mr. and Mrs. Wheelwright in Laburnam Road, Bournville. I was the junior member of the office staff, working with Mrs. Hilda Rees, Miss Gwen Hazelwood and Miss Thomas. There was a home in Herefordshire. Mr. Mathews was a very kind gentleman with a twinkling sense of humour, and he took his staff under his wing as he did 'his' children.

Mrs. Sheila Skoczylas, nee Hougham, from Marston Green, sent three letters, and further research material. The fascinating saga develops. Mr. Mathews did indeed acquire a house, and also boarded children out on many convalescent farms. I was on one near Tenbury Wells in 1932.

May I give you a child's impression of the great man. Mr. Mathews, the Gentle Giant, lover of all children; he spent his life making the weak ones strong, restoring a smile to their faces. He towered above us and being profoundly deaf he had a gruff voice and seemed to roar when he spoke, but we loved him. A giant in stature and heart. His back was bowed with severe pain of Rheumatism or Arthritis and he vowed to ease the pain of suffering and fearful children.

All children were not disabled, there were those who needed long periods of convalescence away from stressful lives, which was damaging their health and well-being.

I had a lot of contact with Mr. Mathews working in his office when I left school at 14 years of age. I can say what I know, from talking to my friends, and I was a patient myself. At some date when Mr. Mathews ran the Invalid Children's Society (as I knew it) he acquired a mansion - Haseley Hall, near Warwick (between Hatton and Wroxall), which has now been altered to private flats. I know that Haseley Hall was still a convalescent Home in 1932 and for several years later in Mr. Mathews' hands. Then around this time, and during the 2nd world war years, children were placed at the Longlands Farm, Greete, (between Burford and Cleehill) near Tenbury Wells, with a lovely caring family. Two sisters took children in on a smaller farm at Diddlesbury (east of Craven Arms on the Much Wenlock Road).

I went to the Longlands in 1932. When one of the Longlands daughters married she eventually took in girls around 1938 - 1939, at Hayton's Bent. (North of Ludlow). and there was another convalescent home near Whitton, again near Tenbury Wells.

Mary Birks, from Northfield, who is the custodian of the Records of the "Birmingham Society for the Care of Invalid and Nervous Children." provides the following newspaper reports:-

Sunday Mercury 27/12/81,

Happy Days at Haseley Hall - Mrs. Agnes Sluman, nee Stanley. The beautiful old Hall that was taken over by the education chiefs of the early 1930's to house 45 girls at a time, suffering from rheumatic heart defects. It was September 1931 that I was taken from smokey old Brum into a fairyland of trees, lawns and rose gardens. Haseley was dressed in her autumn coat of red and pink Virginia creeper and she looked like a castle to me. I left Haseley to make my way in the dreary work-a-day life of Brum in 1934."

Sunday Mercury 3/1/62

"Another Old Haseley Girl. Mrs. Ruby Kendrick, nee Granger.

I have lots of memories of those days, but one I really must share is of Mr. Frank Mathews. He did all the administration, and by his work in arranging charity collections of money, books, and clothes, actually kept the Hall going. We girls at Haseley loved him, and it was a real fight to get hold of his hand and walk with him in the gardens ."

The following statement by Frank Mathews is most relevant to the reasoning behind his resignation from the Cripples Union.

My twenty-five years' experience in visiting crippled children in all parts of the City very early caused me to realise that alongside the problem with which I was dealing was another which was equally grave - the problem of the child suffering from serious illness such as Rheumatism, Chorea (St. Vitus Dance), and Heart Disease.

Indeed in the first ten years some attempt was made to deal with children suffering from Chorea and Heart disease but it was soon found impracticable, as the problem of the crippled child was a specialised one and could not be further complicated, so that it seemed fitting that when the time came for me to relinquish the post of Secretary to the Cripples' Union, some effort should be made to cope with this problem.

As the crippled child becomes deformed externally, so these children become crippled within, but the effect is not so appealing to the eye and purse. It has been impossible to send all our children to Hospitals, and a number have been boarded out in farms or cottages. This is looked upon as experimental work, but so far the results have been encouraging.

Mrs. Susy Crisp, nee' Stevens, from Hungerford, Berkshire stayed at the Smith's Farm, in the Village of Greete, Nr. Ludlow in 1932, for six months before going to Haseley Hall, Nr. Warwick, a lovely place covered with Virginia creeper. I guess it was a form of Boarding School for sick children.

There were roughly 39 girls ranging in age from 8 to 14 years. Mr. Mathews did a great job for lots of children who otherwise would not be alive today.

I went to the Smith's Farm, in the Village of Greet, Nr. Ludlow in 1932

Frank Mathews died on the 5th June 1948, aged 77 years. having been bedridden for the previous six months. *He had been responsible for the opening of Haseley Hall in 1930, and had just received a £15,000 grant from the Ministry of Education, to develop Bodenham Manor, Herefordshire as a residential school. He did not live to see its opening some twelve months later.

* Birmingham Gazette 7th June 1948.

Haseley Manor still stands today (1997), its walls no longer covered with Virginia creeper, with its long winding drive. The Manor house lies but a few miles south of Chadwick End, and that first Convalescent Cottage Home founded by Frank Mathews nearly 50 years before. One of his last activities for the hospital was when he attended the unveiling of a bed, at Woodlands in November 1947, a bed donated by the Chadwick End Women's Institute.

I would like to thank Mr. Roy Calfield for kindly showing me around the Chadwick End Cottage Home, he having purchased the property in the 1950s. (Now owned by his daughter and son-in-law) Coincidentally it was, and still is called 'Woodlands', and as Roy explained, had been built in the late 1890s from the bricks and stone resulting from the demolition of three nearby cottages, originally being called Jubilee Cottage.

Despite modifications and additions, there is still a feeling of tranquillity. One expected to see that Tent in the garden. Roy pointed out the site of the sand-garden, and the some-what changing uninterrupted views across the Warwickshire country-side, from the spacious garden. An idyllic setting for the children A short walk along the road took us to the site of the proposed New Convalescent Home, (in the first decade of this century), on the corner of Oldwych Lane and Chadwick Lane, the large field, still not built upon.

Frank Mathews had devoted almost 50 years of his life, to caring for the unfortunate children of the city.

Frank Mathews at the Woodlands.
Bed Endowment. 1947
Left to Right: (Standing)
Dr. J. F. Brailsford: *Mr. Frank Mathews: Dame Elizabeth Cadbury:
Mr. H. F. Harvey: Mr. Sinclair: Matron (Miss Mountain): Mr. Pike.
* Founder of the Cripples Union.

Naughton Dunn
Source: Naughton Dunn, Orthopaedic Surgeon, His Life and Times
1884-1939 by kind permission of Mr. Peter Dunn
photo: Brian Jones

Chapter 6

Naughton Dunn and Orthopaedics

No history, such as this, could possibly be complete without giving a background as to Orthopaedics, and moreover to those people who have so prominently played a part in laying the foundation in this country. Hugh Owen Thomas, Robert Jones, Agnes Hunt, and with special reference to Naughton Dunn the first orthopaedic surgeon to the Birmingham Cripples Union.

The two sources from which this 'profile' has been gathered, are;-

(1) Naughton Dunn, Orthopaedic Surgeon. His Life and Times,1884 - 1939. based on the inaugural Naughton Dunn Memorial Lecture given by his son Peter M. Dunn, to the British Orthopaedic Association, Southampton, 17th. April 1986.

(2) Lecture given by Mr. Max Harrison in 1984, to honour the birth of Birmingham's most distinguished Orthopaedic Surgeon.

From Peter Dunn's Paper I have taken a look, primarily, at Naughton Dunn 'the Man.' with the general outline of his life. From Max Harrison at the more detailed medical aspects and the nineteenth century background to orthopaedics.

Peter writes: "Naughton Dunn, son of a crofters daughter, and whose father was a very successful Aberdeen shoemaker, was the youngest of a family of eight. Initially having an inclination to go into farming, he enrolled at Aberdeen University subsequently achieving the Master of Arts degree then, unexpectedly, decided to become a doctor. In 1909 at the age of 25, he qualified MB., Ch.B."

Max Harrison started by surveying the changing pattern of orthopaedic disease over 'these 100 years' and examining the way that men and women have tried to wage the battle against it before Naughton Dunn's time and during his career.

"Disease of the locomotive system spares the lives of its sufferers more than many diseases simply because the locomotor system is not immediately concerned with the so-called vital functions. The bones and the joints subserve support and movement, their disease leads to crippling rather than killing, this gives the patients more time to suffer and their numbers to grow, and the surgeons have more years to try and treat. The angel of death, although not completely barred from the field, does not win so many as he does in diseases of other systems. Naughton Dunn waged the war against orthopaedic disease mightily but his efforts cannot be considered apart from those of his teacher, Robert Jones, nor his from those of his teacher, Hugh Owen Thomas."

"Hugh Owen Thomas was born in 1834, last of a line of bone setters. He studied medicine in Liverpool, Edinburgh, London and Paris. Orthopaedic surgery was very much the ugly duckling of Surgery, promising little distinction for anybody who identified with it. The first half of the 19th century had been a dark time for cripples."

"Hugh Owen Thomas's practice was primarily conservative and he considered that the blacksmith's hammer deftly used was in most cases a more powerful reparative instrument than the surgeon's knife. ... His working days stretched from 6 a.m. to midnight and on Sundays he ran his free clinic attended by the poor of Liverpool who queued for hours to see him."

"Ridlon later stated that 'one could gain more useful knowledge from following Thomas round for an hour than anyone else in Great. Britain for months.' He described how on one Sunday five women came in with deformed wrists from badly treated Colles fractures, the wrists were refractured, the deformity corrected and the arms splinted not only without an anaesthetic but without them being told that their arms were to be broken again. Mr. Thomas handed the splints and bandage to me, Ridlon writes, he took his wrench in the right hand and swung it under his coat tail and we went into the waiting room where the women sat against the wall. He put his foot on the seat beside one, took her hand and put it on his thigh, out came the wrench which was slipped on and tightened by a turn of the wrist, a twist, a scream, the wrench dropped to the floor, the bone was set, the hand pronated and the splints put on all in much less time than it takes to tell."

"Robert Jones was a nephew of Thomas, and after qualifying he joined his uncle as a Professional Assistant. Thomas was, in a sense, a prophet: His nephew, Robert Jones, learned the prophet lessons and then became the greatest orthopaedic Surgeon in the world. "

"Thomas died in 1891 and Robert Jones stayed on at Nelson Street developing a vast private practice. At the same time he was on the staff of the Royal Southern Hospital in Liverpool. He applied and developed the methods practiced by his uncle, incorporating each scientific development as it arrived. For instance, he was using and possessed probably the first X-ray set in the country in 1896."

"In the course of his lifetime a veritable army of people worshipped him and the work he was doing. The personality, married to an indefatigable capacity for work and extreme clinical ability, was to carry its owner to fame and personal ascendancy but, more to the point it carried the emergent discipline of orthopaedic surgery, the inheritance of the bone setter and the cast-off of the surgeons of the day, to something very much like the position that it now occupies. How was this done? "

" The 10 years prior to the first world war were those in which the amazing Agnes Hunt, a crippled nurse, started her pioneer work in the Shropshire village of Baschurch where, in a country home, she developed a hospital for the crippled child. The patients were taken at intervals by horse and in a farmer's cart and train to see the great Robert Jones in Liverpool. Eventually she persuaded him to take up a working assignment at Baschurch: this was the beginning of the world's first open-air orthopaedic hospital for crippled children which relied mainly upon the Thomas principles of immobilisation; enforced, uninterrupted and prolonged. Surgical intervention was not denied but was merely an incident. This experiment prospered, profoundly sick children were healed, visitors became converts and similar hospitals were established, in 1906 St. Vincent's Hospital, Pinner, Middlesex., 1908 Lord Mayor Treloar at Alton, 1909 our own Woodlands."

Peter Dunn continues:

"His first post was a senior house surgeon to Mr. Charles Salter in Scarborough Hospital, Yorkshire, one of the many hospitals visited by Robert Jones of Liverpool, the acknowledged Father of Modern Orthopaedic Surgery. Naughton Dunn subsequently eagerly accepted the invitation to become resident surgical officer at the Royal Southern Hospital Liverpool. He would have visited Baschurch Hospital (Oswestry), opened in 1900 as a home for crippled children by two nurses, Miss Agnes Hunt and Miss Goodford. In 1904 Robert Jones was appointed as its first surgeon, he being intensely interested both in the work of this, the first open-air hospital of its kind, and in their efforts on behalf of crippled humanity.

Naughton Dunn was taken on, in 1912, as Robert Jones' private assistant at his famous consulting rooms 11 Nelson Street. Liverpool, rooms that Jones had inherited from his uncle, the great Hugh Owen Thomas of Liverpool. Naughton Dunn also took a post at this time as Assistant Demonstrator in Anatomy in the University of Liverpool.

Max Harrison adds: "At 29, an exponent of the Hugh Owen Thomas/Robert Jones philosophy of orthopaedic surgery, N.D. was perfectly placed to develop this and the open-air hospital techniques he had learned at Baschurch." Peter Dunn continuing: "In October 1913 the Birmingham and District Cripples' Union advertised the post of Honorary Surgeon, he applied and obtained the appointment, coming to the hospital at the age of 29 and being the first orthopaedic specialist in the city.

Within a few months (of his appointment) the Great War broke out. Robert Jones initially persuaded him from joining up, seeing the need there would be for orthopaedic surgeons as the war progressed. Robert Jones was himself becoming increasingly involved with the organisation of Military orthopaedic work in this country and he arranged for Naughton Dunn, along with Girdlestone and Macrae Aitkin, to join the staff at Baschurch, soon to be known as the Shropshire Military Hospital. In Britain many tens of thousands of wounded soldiers were being shipped from France and from a medical and orthopaedic point of view chaos reigned.

Shortly afterwards Colonel Robert Jones was promoted Brigadier and put in charge of the Military Orthopaedic Department at the War Office". The 1914-18 war made history on a variety of accounts, one was the unprecedented toll of dead and injured soldiers. Robert Jones was already the most experienced surgeon in the care of the injured because he had taken the responsibility for treatment of the many navvies injured during the construction in 1887 of the ship canal connecting Liverpool to Manchester. It was natural that he should be given rapidly increasing responsibility for the care of the injured soldiers both in France and on their return. As is well-known the introduction of the Thomas long splint as a first-aid measure reduced the mortality of compound leg fractures in the field from 80% to 20%. In this work he was supported by the men he had trained in Liverpool and Baschurch. Together they were a relative handful and Captain Naughton Dunn was one of them. who to start with, continued his work in Birmingham, then joined the army, saw service abroad in the Middle East, including the Dardanelles but was returned home seriously sick. "

The policy of the British Army Medical Services was, Max states, quite straightforward. If an injured soldier could be healed to a level where he could return to France then he remained within the army but if his injuries were such that he would not be able to serve again he was to be discharged from the army and his surgical care would be undertaken in his own town, wherever that was.

" By 1915 public opinion was exerting itself. Colonel Robert Jones had obtained a previous Poor Law Hospital at Shepherd's Bush which he equipped to receive the wounded soldiers not only to care for them in the phase of immediate need but most importantly to carry on until they were able to return to military service. Here the idea of rehabilitation was developed, the hospital included workshops where the injured men could begin the therapy of work, an entirely unheard of concept in Medicine at this time. Similar centres were established around the country including 800 beds at Highbury Hospital in Birmingham and it was to this unit that Captain Dunn came having served a stint at Shepherd's Bush with Robert Jones."

Peter continues this connection: "In March 1916 Captain Dunn became a founder member of the Shepherd's Bush staff and remained on it for nearly two years, gaining experience and publishing papers on trauma surgery, ranging from nerve suture and correction of deformities of the knee and elbow, to the treatment of malunited fractures of the femur. 'The historical importance of Shepherd's Bush', as Frederick Watson wrote later, 'was that it became the first experimental hospital in training the disabled ... As a pioneer institution it became the model for centres at Manchester, Leeds, Newcastle, Oxford, Cardiff, Birmingham, Bristol, Bath, Edinburgh, Glasgow, Aberdeen, Dublin and Belfast' It was also a 'finishing school' for the orthopaedic surgeons chosen by Robert Jones to take charge of those various centres.

At the end of 1917 Sir Robert Jones transferred Major Dunn to Birmingham as surgeon in charge of all military orthopaedic hospitals in the area. From January 1918 until March 1920, when he was demobbed, Naughton Dunn directed military orthopaedic work in the Midlands, his main base being the 800 bedded *Highbury Hospital. (the Chamberlain family's former home, Kings Heath).

* (Naughton Dunn had married on 3rd September 1919, Ethel Jackson, a daughter of a Birmingham councillor and business man in the wholesale fruit and vegetable trade. Nurse Jackson was working at Highbury being in charge of the plaster room).

In 1920 Naughton Dunn returned to civilian practice in Birmingham. He played a major part in the amalgamation of the Cripples' Union and Royal Orthopaedic and Spinal Hospital,(1925) and maintained his close association with Oswestry where he eventually became the senior surgeon after Sir Robert's retirement. He also took a special pride in helping to set up and develop the Warwickshire Orthopaedic Hospital in Coleshill; and spent some time at St Thomas's setting up and supervising an orthopaedic department there until it was firmly established. During this period the British Orthopaedic Association grew and flourished and he became a member of its Council and contributed papers on a variety of subjects - "... more on stabilising operations of the foot, on the treatment of club foot, on the management of injuries to the upper limb and on fractures of the legs."

In the same year as Sir Robert's 70th birthday (28th June 1928), Naughton Dunn was made President of the Orthopaedic Section of the Royal Society of Medicine. His old Universiy, Aberdeen, honoured him in

1937 by promoting him Doctor of Laws "...in recognition of his steady devotion to the cause of the cripple and his contributions to the knowledge and advance of orthopaedic surgery."

In May 1939 Naughton Dunn wrote of the threatening war, and of the preparations being made, adding " ... but, as usual, we will not be at our best until it has gone on for some time ..."

Sadly he did not have that 'time', on the 18th of November 1939, he died. He was only 54 years old."

Max Harrison now talks about orthopaedics: "Another phase of the life of Robert Jones took place after the war, working with another Baschurch pupil, Gathorne Girdlestone, who had established the Wingfield Orthopaedic Hospital in Oxford. Together they constructed a blue print for a national scheme for the care of cripples. These would be sought out not only in the Outpatients of General Hospitals but in the market places of country towns. They would be diagnosed and treated where found by the doctors and a core of after-care Sisters trained in the Robert Jones and Agnes Hunt traditions. As needed they would be brought into the central hospital for inpatient care. The service went out to the patients. This National Scheme came to fruition and was the basis of orthopaedic care throughout the country for many years. The Royal Orthopaedic Hospital, Birmingham, (Woodlands) under the leadership of Naughton Dunn, was the centre for the work in the Midlands.

The remarkable evolution of orthopaedic surgery over the hundred years since the birth of Naughton Dunn has hinged upon the co-operation of pioneer surgeons with benefactors both small and large. With the advent of the National Health Service the benefaction was thought to be no longer needed. It is a matter for consideration as to what are the national implications of the removal for the need of this type of selfless service and generosity shown by previous generations." (Max had also referred to the hospital evolution, from its foundation in 1817, as representing a wonderful testament to good-heartedness, public spiritedness and generosity of the people).

The following information is particularly interesting in that it gives a "Who's Who" of the Medical Alumni, of 70 years ago.

"Finally how do we evaluate Naughton Dunn and his contribution? In 1926, a surgeon without a Fellowship, Naughton Dunn applied successfully for the post of Lecturer in Orthopaedic Surgery at the University of Birmingham and used as his referees Sir Robert Jones, Honorary President of the British Orthopaedic Association, Dr. Osgood, Professor of Orthopaedic Surgery at Harvard, Mr. Fairbank, the President of the British Orthopaedic Association, Mr. E. Muirhead Little, past-President of the British Orthopaedic Association, Sir. Harold Styles, late Professor of Surgery at the University of Edinburgh, Dr. Murk Jansen, Professor of Orthopaedic Surgery in Holland. A founder member of the British Orthopaedic Association, he was its President at the time of his death and an authoritative contributor to the orthopaedic literature on war injuries, foot problems, and the surgery of paralysis. His principal work had been done at Woodlands, Oswestry, St. Gerrard's and at Hartshill Hospital, Stoke on Trent, and he trained many of the next generation of orthopaedic surgeons, not least Francis G. Allen and Tony Hendry in Birmingham. Sir Harry Platt passed the opinion that Naughton Dunn was closer to Robert Jones than probably any of his pupils.. Never a strong man he made light of his ailments even when the dread disease from which he died fastened its grim tentacles on him. He still came to minister to us , forgetting his own pain and weakness in order to help us who are not nearly so ill as he. Perhaps the greatest work he did for crippled humanity was by passing on Robert Jone's teaching to younger orthopaedic surgeons."

Of the' post Naughton Dunn period' Max says:.

"... He created a base which we still use ... The enemy, orthopaedic disease, has regrouped having suffered severe defeats on various fronts at the hands of other orthopaedic surgeons and other disciples. It is my pleasure to mention especially the contribution of my great teacher, Joseph Trueta, who I regard as the midwife of scientific orthopaedics in this century. His career, particularly from 1938-1967, convinced Orthopaedic Surgeons of the value of collaboration in laboratory studies and took our clinical work into a new orbit. Waksman initiated the defeat of skeletal tuberculosis with streptomycin, Salk eradicated poliomyelitis with the vaccine, antibiotics have more or less disposed of skeletal syphilis and completely changed the problem of pyrogenic infection of bone. Cerebral palsy has suffered at the hands of improved obstetrical care. Rickets is virtually confined to immigrants. Although much childhood disease has been eliminated, disease of the second childhood flourishes; hip and knee osteoarthritics constitute a clamouring queue to get on the operating table ... Care of the injured has been revolutionised by adding to the Thomas/Jones tradition influences from another Liverpool man, Watson-Jones, from the Birmingham Accident Hospital and the Swiss school of internal fixation. Modern techniques are extending operability in a breathtaking way. Hardly a single operation that I was taught as a Registrar is practiced in the same way today ..."

The Chapter of 'Memories', later in this book, contains many comments relating to the humanity and caring nature of Naughton Dunn. None so poignant, however, than that from the lady who, 74 years on, recalled when on having her left foot amputated as an 11 year old "He gave me a sixpenny piece for being so good."

There is no doubt that he was greatly respected by his professional peers.

Two such statements, being:-

From Robert Osgood, following a lecture given by Naughton Dunn in America, in 1934 "... you are one of the finest Naughton, and I should be a better man if you lived round the corner."

From Rowley Bristow "... He leaves behind a name and a standard for his friends to try to live up to."

Chapter 7

NHS.
1948 - 1970

Mr. H. F. Harvey has already been quoted in his 'Foreword' to the 23rd Annual Report of the Royal Cripples Hospital, 1947 responding to the forthcoming NHS. At a Commemorative Dinner held at the Midland Hotel on September 29th, 1948, he spoke, to the gathering 'of members of the former management and sub-committees of the Royal Cripples Hospital, and senior staff.'

His comments I feel provide a fitting close to the past, including tributes, as it does, to many of the people who had, over the previous 30 years, contributed to its success and to the many achievements and looking to the future success of the new Health Service.

Having been presented with a gift of a pair of Binoculars, and fitting praise for his own services, Mr. Harvey commented "... He was particularly interested to receive it at the hands of one their friends (Dr. H. Guy Dain) from over the Border, for during the whole of his association with the Hospital, Scottish members - first John Weatherhead and John Scott, then T. N. Veitch and Murray-Laing, had taken a leading part in its work, whilst Scottish Surgeons had always been prominent."

Harking back to his earliest association in 1919, Mr. Harvey said that his pleasantest recollections were of the many friends he had made and the happy relations that had always existed. They had their worries in those days and more than once he and the late Frank Mathews were called into the Bank Managers 'Sweating Chamber' on account of their overdraft. There had been troubles between Teachers and Nurses at Forelands too, but in recent years these had faded out.

It was a great day when in 1929 the Duchess of York opened the first of the extensions; The Rotary Wards, Men's and Women's Wards, Nurses' Home, New Operating Theatre, and Massage Departments and Gymnasium. The next 10 years had seen further development including the Private Patient's Block, the Maid's Hostel, and the first of the New Angle

Wards, and with the war-time building restrictions the erection of Prefabricated Hutment's.

"Now they had come to the parting of the ways. The control, of the Administration had passed to a new Management Committee ... responsible for twelve other hospitals altogether. This meant that, to their great regret, many of those who had been associated with the development of the Hospital they loved had to part company. So far they had been unable to persuade the new Management Committee to set up a House Committee for the Royal Cripples Hospital but it had appointed an 'Interim Liaison Advisory Committee' on which the services of a number of those who had been prominently associated with the administration were retained - at least for the time being - and it was proposed to establish a *League of Friends, which it hoped would link together, for the benefit of patients, ex-patients, staff and home-bound cripples, all who had worked for and supported the Hospital in the past.

He had no doubt that their Hospital would , in the future play a worthy part in the new Health Service for the country which the Government had recently (5th July 1948) brought into being."

A most appropriate contribution to the evening activity was that of Dame Elizabeth Cadbury who spoke "... of the beginnings of the Woodlands and of the wonderful voluntary support and service which had been given to the Hospital..."

* The formation of the League of Friends at Woodlands was 26 years in the future. This comment was, however, prompted by the probable knowledge, that the National Association of the League of Friends was to be formed in 1949. Implying that there were some already in existence.

Matron's Reports for 1948/9, highlight some interesting events. The Linen League was busy replacing linen which had been lost due to a fire at the Supreme Laundry, Miss Barrows having obtained ex-Government Stock Theatre Gowns. Losses having been incurred in the Private Wards, 6, 7, 8, Cloister Wards, Plaster, X-ray and Massage Departments, together with some Sisters' Uniforms. The new building for the Nursing School, in use from August 31st, welcomed 22 New Student Nurses from Woodlands, and 2 from Forelands.

Woodlands from the Air

Source: Royal Cripples Hospital Annual Reports 1930-1934

photo: Brian Jones

The number of students at Belmont had outgrown the building, Matron advising the transferring of the school to Bella Vista, and using Belmont as a residential hostel only, "... it would appear to afford better facilities for class-rooms and recreation rooms ... enabling the Physiotherapy School facilities for taking male students. The change over would not necessitate acquisition of a new gymnasium, at Bella Vista, the present one being converted into cubicles.... the present Common Room arrangements at Belmont are poor."

April 1949 had seen a Birmingham Nurses' Protest Meeting. There was apparently no support from the Hospital, however Miss Mountain felt that there were some grounds for discontent among "... some members of our trained staff with regard to salaries ..." Mr. Wilson Stuart was treated in the Woodlands, in June 1949, "... The Nursing Staff esteem it a privilege to have been able to nurse Mr. Stuart through his period of convalescence ..." A Plaque bearing the name 'Elizabeth Cadbury House' was placed above the main doorway of what was originally the Maids' Hostel, late 1949, "... We are very proud that one of the Staff Residences bears this loved and honoured name".

Additional source material is the 'Minutes' of Meetings of the Birmingham (Selly Oak) Hospital Management Committee , the first of which identifies Albert F. Bradbeer, (Lord Mayor of the City of Birmingham, 1946/47), as Chairman, with a memo. to Miss Whittock, Secretary of the Royal Cripples Hospital, stating that the Deputy Matron, Miss Beal had resigned, Miss Hyden being appointed in her place. The Matron, Miss Mountain, was to be consulted as to the post of Second Assistant Matron, vacated by Miss Hyden, (Miss Dean being subsequently appointed). We also hear that the former Sister-in-Charge at Belmont, Miss Overall had moved to Forelands as Assistant Matron. Other changes being the appointment of Miss Waller, formerly the first Warden at the Bella Vista Hostel, as Warden at Belmont, Miss Longstaffe moving as Warden at Bella Vista. Those early days were certainly seeing many changes. The gardens were not forgotten either. Bulbs being purchased for Woodlands at a cost of £27-13-9d. and with the resignation of the Chief Engineer, who had also been in charge of all the male staff, Mr. Frearson, a member of the Porters Staff was promoted to the post of Head Porter.

In early 1949 Miss Mountain was authorised to appoint Sister Gascoyne as a Second Sister Tutor, her previous position as Second Plaster Sister, being filled by Staff Nurse Bailey. A third telephone operator was to be appointed at Forelands, (see also Chapter 8, for the memories of Mrs. Edna Dawson), to enable the switchboard to be manned from 7.30am. to 10pm. as a temporary measure. Shortly after, this position was made permanent.

Miss Whittock was appointed the representative of the Royal Cripples Hospital, on the Central Council for the Care of Cripples. Dr. Brailsford proposed that the establishment of the X-ray Department staff should be - 4 trained radiographers, including radiographer-in-charge and 3 students, the staff "at present" being radiographer-in-charge and 5 students, but 2 of the students "had now qualified." An electric washing machine and replacement dish-washing machine was required in the babies ward at Woodlands, and bed-lights and wireless plugs for nurses' bedrooms, at Woodlands and Forelands.

The most significant event of the year being that 'on Founders Day, 1949', the Woodlands, Royal Cripples Hospital was renamed 'The Royal Orthopaedic Hospital.'

During the next year, permission was given for the purchase of 12 store-pigs at Forelands at an approximate cost of £5 each, and one dozen Nurses' Cloaks, at 65/5d (?) each, ordered. Bella Vista was to get its share of bicycle racks, and telephones were again on the agenda. The Hospital Management Committee giving consideration to the principle of contributing towards the cost of telephones in the homes of non-resident administrative officers, 'in the case of certain designated posts'. Miss Whittock had clearly staked her claim, the Committee stating that, in her case, "... they would be prepared to meet the cost of rental only, as from 1st January 1950 ... the telephone should be in your own name and the account should be rendered to and paid by you ..."

Matron's Reports for 1950 announced on April 28th, the retirement of Miss Morley and Miss Margerison as Head Teacher and 1st Assistant Teacher. Miss Morley after 12 years and Miss Margerison having been there since the opening of the school in 1914. The original Curtains in

Rabone Hall which had been up since its opening in 1931 were "... very faded and showing signs of wear. May these please be renewed ?" The Boiler Chimney at Belmont is giving cause for concern as its smoke is making life unpleasant in the bedrooms, and the soot, when the flue is swept once a week, is extremely troublesome. Complaints from students made in the winter had not been addressed by the summer. A request for a Telephone extension to the 'Internal house telephone' from the ground floor to the Doctors' Bedrooms on the first floor was made. The Doctors' being unable to hear it at night.

Supplies of Milk to Hospitals came under discussion following views from the Ministry of Health and the British Medical Association. The Hospital Management Committee declaring that the question of the purchase of T. T. milk that had been sterilised or pasteurised was too big a problem to be decided on a local basis, the matter being referred to the Association of Hospital Management Committees for consideration on a national basis.

The Management Committee Minutes record in 1951 (Moving from milk to tea), that a better quality of tea should be supplied to hospitals in the future. That authorisation be given to accept the most suitable tenders for the supply of Jams and Marmalade and Soft Drinks, for a period of six months from 1-2-51. Concern re Christmas entertainment is seen by "... that the provision of entertainment for non-dancers as an alternative to the Tower Ballroom Dances, be approved in principle."

The Clinical Staff Sub-committee, were a little concerned in January 1951, they having reported that the Hospital Car DAB 827, housed at the Woodlands, primarily for the use of the Residential Medical Staff, had recently required extensive repairs, and that following the completion of these had not been returned to the Hospital. All was well however, as on 11th April it is reported that Hospital Car DAB 827 is now in the Group Transport Pool.

Following the retirement of Miss Pocock, Matron at Forelands on 31st March 1951, the nursing staffs at Woodlands and Forelands were to operate under the general supervision of the Matron at Woodlands. Mr. W. H. Scrase (the present Registrar) was appointed full-time Assistant Orthopaedic Surgeon at Senior Hospital Medical Officer status. The death was announced of Mr. Veitch, former Vice-Chairman of the Hospital Management Committee, and the new Physiotherapy Department which he had lived to see opened at Selly Oak Hospital, was to be honoured with his name.

The membership of sub-committees was given as:-

Medical Sub-Committee
Alderman G.E.Beavon
Dr. J.F.Brailsford
Dr.G.G.Gillam
Dr. L.Hallum
Mr. R.R.S.Kelman
Dr. J.McGarrity
Councillor A.Shanks
Dr. Donald Stewart

Works and Buildings
Alderman G.E.Beavon
Councillor J.Brewin
Councillor H.N.Cartwright
Mr. J.H.Crompton
Dr. J.McGarrity
Councillor F.F.Griffin

Finance and Purchasing
Dr. G.G.Gillam
Mr. C.H.Russell
Councillor W.F.Smith
Councillor F.F.Griffin
Alderman Mrs. N.Hyde

Staff Sub-Committee
Mr. H.Baker
Dr. L.Hallum
Mr. H.F.Harvey
Alderman Mrs. N.Hyde
Mr. R.R.S.Kelman
Mr. J.R.Leach
Miss M.R.Tilling.

Concerning the provision of Dentures "... prosthetic work be carried out for resident staff in the Hospitals in the Group for emergency purposes, for a period of one year ..." Also the Group Pathology Services Selly Oak Hospital Laboratory was to become the Group Laboratory staffed 'exactly as at present' but that the Senior Technician promoted to Deputy Chief Technician of Selly Oak Hospital and responsible for detail.

No. 622 Bristol Road South, was to be supplied with 5 Divans and 19 Rugs at a total cost of £92-15-0. And approval in principle was given that nurses securing their Orthopaedic Nursing Certificates at the R.O.H.

Woodlands, be given Badges, free of charge. Past students being allowed to purchase at cost price.

A September 'Minute' records the establishment of a Preliminary Nurses' Training Group School, at Midland Hospital, The Reddings, and three months later "... the appointment of a third Physiotherapist as a temporary measure..." at the Orthopaedic Clinic, Blossomfield House, Solihull. Architects plans are also under preparation for a New Children's Block at Woodlands.

December 16th, 1951 marked a sad event. when following the death of Dame Elizabeth Cadbury (4th December) a Memorial Service was held at the Cadbury Works. Members of the Nursing Staff in uniform, and of the Clerical and Domestic Staffs, being present.

Revised 'in' and 'out' access arrangements for motor vehicles, at this time, referred to the need for a second entrance to the Lower Drive, and the drive adjoining the Lodge straightened to lead to the general car-park on the North side of the Theatre Block.

The Clinical Staff Sub-Committee, instructs the Stenographer's (early in 1952), that, in the case of Honorary Surgeons, they should type the word 'Surgeon' under the signature of Consultants correspondence in future. Dr.C.P.Cotterill was appointed as Senior House Officer, and the Inpatient and Outpatient statistics for 1950/51 were given as " ... an increase in the total number of operations, from 1,606 to 2,210, a development that had inevitably involved a lower bed occupancy 227.65 to 209.72." A Special Service was held in the Hospital Chapel on February 15th, 1952 following the death of King George VI , conducted by the Rev. Mr. Buckler. The Matron, Miss Fountain had an accident in March falling on the steps to Elizabeth Cadbury House and suffering lacerations to her face, which required treatment at the Accident Hospital. Miss Hyden, the Assistant Matron taking charge. Mr. G. Percival Mills death was announced in April 1952.

The announcement of a burglary, in the July resulted in the advice that an enquiry Office be set up at the Front door. Sister Dean's bedroom had been entered, £9 stolen together with her Identification Card and Post-Office book. The bag was found on a building site in Northfield. At the end of the year the Woodlands Teaching Staff put on a party for Miss Bull who had left the teaching staff after 38 years service.

Miss Mountain had appointed Mrs. P. O. Hewett as Sister-in-Charge of the Hospital's Outpatient Clinics. A serious shortage of Senior Nursing Staff prompted the Matron to suggest that either a complete closure of one ward at Woodlands, or the restriction of theatre sessions, to five a week, for a two month period, be considered. The heating of Open-Air Wards seem an anomaly. However in November 1952 the Group Engineer had asked that the heat in the Women's Ward at Forelands should be turned off when the screens fronting on to the Solarium are open, the effort to maintain the radiators at a good heat with the windows overlooking the Solarium open, being an extravagant use of fuel. The Committee recommended that the heating in the Open-Air Wards should be maintained continuously during the winter months on medical grounds.

A most exciting party was given at the Forelands on Boxing Day, 1952. 'A Television Party.' held in the Recreation Hall it was televised during a Children's Hour Programme. "... The children were dressed in beautiful fancy costumes and taken from the Wards to the Hall. The little girls were dressed in party frocks as Fairies etc., The dresses being made by their mothers, and the boys were dressed as Cowboys, Pirates and Toy Soldiers. etc., many of the boys costumes being made by the School Teachers.

The Hall was very nicely decorated as 'Christmas in Toyland' and the entertainment was provided by the B.B.C. The Announcer was Jennifer Gay, the popular Children's Hour Television Announcer. Mr. Barrie Edgar was in charge of the Party, and all arrangements for the Televising of the same. Mr. Edgar questioned two of the boys, John Hannaford, Pirate, and John McCarthy, Demon King, regarding their complaints, the length of their stay in Hospital, and how soon they were likely to be discharged. I am quite sure that the parents' of these children must have been thrilled to see them on the screen.

The small children sang a little Christmas Song, and for this Miss Hall, School Teacher, played the piano. The children also joined in the singing of 'Jingle Bells' and 'Rudolph the Red-Nosed Reindeer.'

The Music was provided by Harry Engleman & his Players. The Artiste's included: Ethel Revnell; Charlie Clapham; Munday & Earle; Danny Gray and Harry Corbett and *Sooty."

*Sooty was to make another appearance at the Woodlands when much later he came to the Hospital to visit Harry Corbett, who was at that time a patient, having had a minor knee operation.

The following year, the Ministry of Health called for the views of hospital Medical Committees on the question of supplying Pethadine and Morphia in Solution, suggesting more effective control if supplied in Ampoules. This was accepted and confirmed by this Hospital adding, as an alternative, the use in tablet form.

Architect's plans for the New Ward Block were creating some concern, regarding the possibility of a ramp being provided from the first floor. This was ruled out as impracticable in terms of cost, and that the full requirements of the fire authorities were being met. A request for two lifts was turned down by a Ministry of Health ruling.

On February 26th, 1954, damage was caused to the examination rooms, X-ray Department, and adjoining premises at Broad Street, due to the fall of an adjacent wall. The temporary transfer of the clinics to rooms in the Physiotherapy Department inevitably resulted in the reduction in the physiotherapy work. The Royal College of Surgeons is to be contacted asking what steps can be taken to have this Hospital recognised as a Training Hospital for the Final F.R.C.S. examination. A letter was received on the 29th, July granting recognition from the F.R.C.S. "... under paragraph 23 (a) of the regulations in respect of the Posts of Senior Registrar, Registrar and Three Senior House Officers."

The Robert Jones and Agnes Hunt Orthopaedic Hospital, Oswestry, had been approached regarding the Cullen 'D' type Lifting apparatus installed in their Hydrotherapy Department, it being proposed that one should be fitted at Woodlands. The question of shoes for adult patients was under consideration, when a local shoe supplier was contacted with a view to their supplying 'odd' shoes. The response being that a supply of odd shoes could be authorised in case of urgency, but the firm would prefer to make to special order, to ensure a better match. A later correspondence stated that, regarding standard shoes in odd sizes at stock prices, requirements would be supplied, whenever possible.

Birmingham University Graduate, Mr. A. C. Pelides, was appointed as Senior House Officer, as from July 10th, 1954, having had experience at the Birmingham United Hospitals and Corbett Hospital, Stourbridge. The emergency admission of patients was raised in committee when the Chairman stated that difficulties arose when doctors desiring patients admitted other than from the waiting list did not make the necessary arrangements direct with the wards. It was agreed that in every case, the doctor concerned should make his own arrangements with the Ward Sister or her Deputy. The need for the Form of Consent to Operative Treatment to be signed by all patients or their relatives, both operative and non operative cases, prior to admission.

At the 25th Anniversary of the opening of Belmont, 120 Old Students of the School of Physiotherapy held their re-union, with a lunch in the Rabone Hall, and following a visit to the wards, tea at Belmont. One month later Mr. F. Wilson, M.D., F.R.C.S. who had been present at that re-union passed away, in the Queen Elizabeth Hospital.

At the end of 1954, Miss Hyden as Acting Matron reports that "... Miss Mountain has returned to us from the General Hospital, Birmingham, to be nursed under the care of Mr. Leather," adding, "... although Miss Mountain easily tires, she keeps very bright and cheerful." On the 12th January, 1955, the Committee Chairman announced, with great regret, the passing on December 20th of Miss W.B.Mountain. Miss L. J. Galbraith was to enter on her duties as Matron as from July 25th, 1955, moving from her position of Assistant Matron at the Prince of Wales Orthopaedic Hospital, Cardiff. In the meantime Miss Hyden was Acting Matron and Miss I. Dean Assistant Matron.

The lease of 622 Bristol Road South was to be discontinued, by the 'minute' entry for 26th January 1955, and in the following March the Birmingham Corporation Parks Department were asked to undertake a survey of the gardens, in the Group, and to advise on the most economical deployment of the gardening staffs.

The next entry is quite charming; " We have been invited by the children of Gurnsey to be members of their ' Love Apple' League, and will be happy to join in. We shall look forward to the gifts we shall receive from the children through this League."

At that same meeting the first move was made for a 'Memorial to Medical Staff, by Mr. Hendry, it being agreed to recommend that Boards should be erected in the entrance Hall at Woodlands Hospital and in the Board Room at Broad Street, giving the names of former senior medical staff with the dates they had served the hospital. Four months later, a list had been circulated of former and present members of the medical staff whose names it was suggested should be placed on the boards. It was agreed to recommend that 2 boards should be provided, one to contain the names of Surgeons, including Ophthalmic and Aural Surgeons, the other the names of Physicians, including Radiologists and Anaesthetists. The list for each board would total about 25 names but it would be necessary to leave room for further names to be added later.

At the next meeting the Chairman expressed the view that there were advantages of having a second board, on which the names of medical staff other than Surgeons, some of whom had served the hospital for a comparatively short time, were included. He felt it might be possible to include those with a length of service of ten years or more on one board. Ten months on from the initial suggestion, it was recommended that one board should be provided with a column for the Surgeons and another column for the Physicians including Anaesthetists and Radiologists.

The future of Radiological Services was raised in September 1955, by the Hospital Management Committee, stating that "... the Advisory Appointments Committee set up by the Regional Hospital Board had recommended a joint appointment of a part-time Consultant Radiologist to the United Birmingham Hospitals and the Birmingham (Selly Oak) Group of Hospitals. It being proposed that 'Dr. P. Jacobs, M.R.C.P., D.M.R.D. be appointed ... and should give five notational half-days weekly to this and the Accident Hospitals and four notational half-days to the United Birmingham Hospitals." Mr. Jacobs was to enter upon his duties on December 1st, and it was recommended that Dr. J.F.Brailsford be appointed Honorary Consultant Radiologist to this hospital at that date.

In the Spring of 1956 Miss Galbraith in looking for a Night

Superintendent appointed a 'home grown' nurse, Miss R. Ballard, from Paddington Green Children's Hospital, who had done her orthopaedic training at this Hospital, being a Gold Medallist in 1950. Subsequently moving to the Birmingham General Hospital Miss Ballard became a S.R.N. later obtaining certificates in Tropical Diseases and Midwifery.

Mr. Leather retired on July 1st, 1956, being replaced, as Consultant Surgeon by Mr. W.H.Scrase.

The question of drugs was again raised, this time by Miss Galbraith, asking for a change to more modern methods of use, than the tablet form of morphia. A sample of the cartridge form and use of syringe being advocated on a trial basis. Miss Littlewood retired from her post as Joint Principal and Head Physiotherapist on 30th September, 1956. As at February 1957 , with the prospective retirement of Miss Fletcher, the Principal of the Physiotherapy School, in July, Miss Littlewood's post not yet having been replaced, it was proposed to advertise for a Principal of the School and Superintendent of Physiotherapy Departments. Also recommended that a Post of Deputy Principal and Superintendent should be established.

The Forelands was one of three Midland Orthopaedic Hospitals visited by the Outside Broadcasting Department of the B.B.C. at the end of 1955, surveying with the view of submitting a report concerning the possibility of Mr. Wilfred Pickles giving a broadcast following the Queen's Speech on Christmas Day, it being only an investigation.

Miss Galbraith was also having to assess the effects of a consideration being given to the re-habilitation of elderly female patients, and the need to set a ward aside at Forelands, following primary treatment at the Accident Hospital. There were problems nursing elderly patients at Forelands which would require the remodelling of nursing patterns. Forelands not being recognised by the General Nursing Council meant that she could not send nurses over 18 years of age to the Unit, and 17 year old nurses would have to be sent, and they were not suitable for nursing elderly patients. Trained Staff would have to be increased, additional Nursing Auxiliaries engaged, Night Staff would have to be increased. At the present elderly patients sent out to Forelands were carefully selected and sent back to Woodlands immediately if they became medically ill.

The House Committee had the sad task of sending a letter to Mr.H.F.Harvey, in January 1957, regretting that he had found it necessary to resign his membership of that Committee, and conveying their deep appreciation of the many years of valuable service. Mr. Harvey, as has been shown in these pages, had in fact given some 38 years, exceptional, service, leading always from the front and of course in co-ordinating the support of the Birmingham people, through the X'mas Tree Fund, that effectively gave the Cripple's Union the boost that it so badly needed.

A surprise comment is to be found in a 'minute' of 30th, January 1957. "... the market gardening be discontinued throughout the Group as soon as possible." and, in June, the General Purpose Sub-Committee agrees to purchase an Electric Pump for the Courtyard Fountain at a cost of £16-10s-0d.

It has been rare throughout this history to have found any detailed information on the appointment of Surgeons, other than a statement of fact re appointment and retirement. So fortunately it is satisfying to, at this period, find so much information on the next appointee, some twelve months before taking up his Post.

12th June 1957, The Chairman said that Mr. M.H.M.Harrison, F.R.C.S. had been recommended for the Joint Consultant Appointment with the United Birmingham Hospitals. It was not known when he would enter upon his duties. One month later 'Max' Harrison having visited Birmingham, met medical staff, and discussed the proposal with the Secretary of the U.B.H. that he should spend some time visiting hospital's abroad. It was agreed that he should complete his 'foreign' tour before taking up his duties.

Surprisingly there are almost immediate requests, from the General Hospital, re his associate partnership, for information as to the days on which Mr. Harrison will be engaged in the out-patient clinic and operating theatre at this hospital. It is stated at the September Committee meeting that that Mr. M.H.M. Harrison would be taking up his appointment on 14th April, 1958, and that he will be visiting the U.S.A. in the New year. Max was subsequently welcomed, by the Clinical Staff Sub-Committee chairman, on that date.

On October 1st, 1957 Miss B. J. Horsfall took up her post as Principal of the Physiotherapy School and Head Physiotherapist. One month later, Miss M. K. Bray was appointed Second Assistant Matron at Woodlands. The keeping of pets, Alarm Bags and Hospital - Traffic Signs, take up committee time. Third party insurance being required by the owner for any dog kept on hospital premises. That the keeping of pets be approved, with the proviso, that, at Forelands, dogs be kept under control and not have access to wards. The purchase of two alarm bags for transport of wages and cash, each at a cost of £26-5-0 size No.3. for the Group Wages Department at Selly Oak. The Royal Orthopaedic and Little Bromwich General Hospitals to get size No.2., at £23-2-0 each, with Solihull Hospital, size No.1., at £17-17-0. For £5 each, two enamel signs bearing the name of the hospital to be sited on the grass reservation in Bristol Road South near the Woodlands.

Miss J.M.Jones the newly appointed Outpatient Superintendent took up her duties on July 8th, 1958, and in the following September the paying of expenses incurred by relatives of patients undergoing treatment at Forelands were being considered. The Hospital Administrator, Miss Whittock, said however, that there were certain provisions under the Ministry of Health regulations for assistance with rail fares, but apparently not for bus fares. The Medical Stenographer at Woodlands, Miss Langston, was under pressure due to the number of interruptions she received by telephone enquiries. This was partially alleviated by arranging for assistance from a second clerk from the Round Tower Office, when not required for that duty.

In the Matron's Reports covering July/August/September 1958, Miss Stiff is recorded as having retired after 23 years with the School of Physiotherapy. These Reports also identify that during the illness of Miss Hyden, Assistant Matron, Miss Dean (Ex-Assistant Matron) had returned, temporarily, to help. A request is also made for improvements in the Rabone Hall "...Could some form of water heating be installed in the cloakrooms, to supply hot-water to the washhand basins?" A piano to replace the "... existing one which is very old and unsatisfactory." is to go into Rabone Hall.

In March 1959 following Mr. Scrase's comment re the pressure on the Medical Stenographer and the difficulties experienced by Registrar's in dictating medical notes, it was felt that as it would not be easy to increase the Clerical establishment, that a Dictaphone be purchased.

Max Harrison was also keeping his eyes open around the Hospital, and bought to the attention of the Administrator the condition of the Hospital name sign. "...The lettering indicating the name of the hospital on the front of the Administration Block at Woodlands had been in need of repair for some weeks. Several letters were missing."

Following the Memorial Board, a Photographic Gallery was under consideration in July 1959, the Administrator being asked to consult the Secretary of the United Birmingham Hospitals concerning photographs of some of the former members of the staff who were also members of that hospital. The initial response being that the only portrait available at the Queen Elizabeth Hospital was that of -

Mr. Jordan Lloyd. The General Hospital did have portraits of seven former members.

The full-time Medical Staff as from 10th, February 1960, are given as:- Mr. Allan; Mr. Hendry; Mr. Donovan; Mr. Scrase; Mr. Harrison. with 1st Assistants, respectively, Mr. Kerkin; Mr. McGregor; Mr. Cotterill; Miss Mehta and Mr. Menon. The pending retirement of Miss Whittock, on 31st March 1960, was announced. Transport was being requested for resident members of hospital staff, including Registrars, who were having difficulty, in the early morning rush-hour, keeping their 9 am. duties at the Broad Street Clinics.

The keeping of pets, on certain wards, was raised, but with particular respect to Budgerigars. It was resolved; "that this committee feels unable to make any recommendation on this matter."

Miss Hyden, Assistant Matron, retired on the 30th November 1960, having been with the Physiotherapy School. She had trained at the original Orthopaedic Hospital, and been at Woodlands since 1931. Miss Horsfall placed a list of items required, by the Physiotherapy Department, at Broad Street, Woodlands and Forelands.

'For Immediate Implementation; Installation of a Lift at Broad Street;

Widening of a gymnasium door, at Woodlands, in order to admit beds; The restoration to the Physiotherapy Department of the existing soap and hardware store. 6 additional full-length mirrors and 3 static cycles, at Broad Street; 2 static cycles at Woodlands and 1 additional Full-Length Mirror at Forelands.' ' For Implementation when additional accommodation can be provided: Parallel Bars at Woodlands and Broad Street; Steps with a hand-rail at Broad Street; Additional rehabilitation equipment including bath, toilets and chairs.'

A comment re Workshop-Orders and Delivery Dates, is a reminder of numerous similar 'excuses' from yester-year. "... It was noted that delays were being experienced in the delivery of certain types of appliances. It was pointed out that this was largely due to the recent employment of two trainees in the metal shop." Mr. Hendry was due to retire on the 11th, November 1961.

During 1961/62 the Woodlands and Forelands received visits from a number of 'stars.' Dickie Henderson. Eric Sykes and Jill Carson. On October 1st, 1962 Miss Jean Guthrie Shaw, S.R.N., S.C.M., O.N.C. commenced her duties as Assistant Matron, having trained at Stockport Infirmary and the Robert Jones and Agnes Hunt Hospital, Oswestry, where she later held senior appointments. Other experiences included work in New Zealand, and appointments at Harlow Wood Orthopaedic Hospital, Nottingham and the Children's Hospital, Marple, Cheshire. Miss Galbraith was of course still Matron, but was clearly not enjoying good health. Over the next few years, until her resignation in 1968, the Matron's Reports' are signed numerous times by the Assistant Matron's, including Miss P. M. Reed who had held the post from 1st July 1962. Miss Reed, previously the Plaster Department Superintendent, having been appointed following the retirement of Miss M. K. Bray.

The Clinical Staff Sub-Committee were giving consideration, in January 1962, to a Joint Memorandum drawn up by the Medical Defence Union and the Royal College of Nursing on steps which might be taken to obviate the risk of an operation on the wrong patient or side, Limb or Digit. In the following April, the Cross Keys Hotel were invited to attend a handing-over ceremony of the Greenhouse that they had presented to the hospital.

The Clinical Staff Sub-Committee in their deliberations 1962/64, noted that notice had been received from the Town Clerk that the Welfare Department wished to relinquish the tenancy of the Handicraft Shop, at 80 Broad Street from the 31st July 1962. A letter was also received from the Management Committee, Selly Oak, regarding the Regional Hospital Board's possible development of Rubery Hill Hospital "... It was understood that this envisaged the provision of 300 orthopaedic beds and a new Physiotherapy School, and the consequential closure of Woodlands, and possibly the Outpatient Department at Broad Street." The Committee was, of course strongly opposed, responding by bringing to the attention of the R.H.B. that:

The report had been prepared without consultation. The Staff had been led to believe that there is no question of the Royal Orthopaedic Hospital being moved in the next 10 to 15 years, and that new theatres and a new Physiotherapy School are to be provided on the Woodlands site in the near future. Disturbance of the R.O.H. would mean; Increase in distance, and difficulties of transfer for inpatients and outpatients. The Physiotherapy School would be more inaccessible from other hospitals for training. The difficulty in retaining specialist nursing and auxiliary staff would be increased. The assets of the existing site would be lost.

The Minutes of the House Committee of the 22nd January 1962 pursue this so called 'Hospital Plan for England and Wales' to its conclusion, Further to the C.S.S-C. comments, the 'Plan' as it relates to the South Birmingham Area, provides for the building of a new major Hospital at Rubery, and the redevelopment of Selly Oak Hospital (incorporating the Royal Orthopaedic Hospital) as a hospital for traumatic and reconstructive surgery, and including the regional and plastic surgery centre. The statement of beds expected following such moves, included no mention of the R.O.H. This had left the House Committee to assume that the intention was to transfer the accommodation at Woodlands and Forelands to Selly Oak.

On the 31st May 1962 the Birmingham Regional Hospital Board, the Hospital Committee and Group Medical Committee met, two resolutions being submitted: "... unable to see any advantage ... to transfer this hospital to Selly Oak ..." and "... see distinct impediments to the maintenance of the present orthopaedic service in such a move and is of the opinion that the present site offers facilities for fuller development of the hospital service." A month later the R.H.B. were asking the R.O.H. to consider a ten year plan.

In August 1963, Mr. Donovan as Chairman of the Clinical Staff Sub-Committee, having attended a meeting of the R.H.B. and H.M.C. announced that "The original proposal that the R.O.H. be resited on the Selly Oak site had now been discarded." The present plans for a major General Hospital to be developed at Rubery still stood pending the development of which the Birmingham General Hospital would continue on the city centre site. The Regional Board's capital programme included provision of additional theatre facilities at Woodlands in 1967/68, and the Board was negotiating with the Bournville Village Trust regarding the extension of the Lease at Belmont. Should it not be possible to obtain an extension for at least 15 years the likelihood was that a new Physiotherapy School would be built at Woodlands.

Discussions with the B.V.T. clearly moved apace, as at the 26th September 1963, an extension of no longer than three years having been offered, the R.H.B. was looking to the building of a new Pysiotherapy School on a piece of land at the rear of Woodlands, which it understood could be leased from the B.V.T. On the 23 rd. April 1964 the R.H.B. had accepted the offer of the B.V.T. to renew the lease of Belmont for a further three years, and had also decided to accept the offer to lease a suitable area of land at the rear of Woodlands for 21 years on which to build the Physiotherapy School.

We have to move forward to November 1965 , to learn that

"... At a meeting with the R.H.B. it was learned that the Ministry of Health were not prepared to build the new Physiotherapy School on other than freehold land. They had therefore ruled out the possibility of the School being erected on the piece of land offered on the Lease by the B.V.T."

All however was not lost. It was recommended to the Hospital Management Committee that the plans for the new School should be 're-cast' on the assumption that it would be built on the tennis court site.

The General Purposes Committee had deferred consideration of the installation of a swimming pool in the Rabone Hall, at their March 1963 meeting, pending further information on the future of the hospital, a tentative scheme having been submitted at an estimated cost of £5,000. On 23rd May 1963 it was stated that the income from the sum of £500 bequeathed by the late Dr. James Brailsford was for the purchase of the Stewart/Brailsford medal annually. These 'gold and silver' medals had been ordered by Dr. Brailsford, and were now as part of his Estate, with his Solicitors. Dr. Brailsford, a Duddeston, Birmingham born man had died on the 28th January 1961 at the age of 73 years.

Boy Scout Activities are thriving at Woodlands in February 1964 with Mr. Nicholls, the Scoutmaster, submitting a request for the purchase of certain equipment in connection with the establishment of a weather station. The request was considered, together with the Scout Association, following which his plans were somewhat watered down, and in fact, 'The scouting activities in Ward 5 be restricted to Sunday evenings between the hours of 6.30 pm. and 8 pm.' Six months later 'the revised plans having been successfully in operation' the Scouting activities, in Ward 5, were being successfully continued.

There was concern expressed regarding the fact that the only public toilets available at Woodlands were those adjoining the physiotherapy block, and that this caused considerable inconvenience to visitors to Wards 11 and 12.

An application for planning permission to establish an Amusement Arcade adjoining the Outpatient Department, Broad Street was rejected by the City Council, and the plans for the swimming pool in the Rabone Hall were abandoned following the Architects opinion that with the need for additional under-pinning of the building the total cost was likely to be around £8,000.

The suggestion was made that a Nurses' League be established at the hospital, membership being open to those who had undergone nurses' training at Woodlands. That the first meeting of the Nurses' League be associated with an Annual Reunion to be held in May 1965 at which hospitality for approximately 200 should be provided. An excellent Annual

Newsletter, was compiled by Miss P. M. Reed, initially on 'foolscap format,' but by 1967 the printed magazine format, marked 'real progress', the words used by Miss L.J.Galbraith (past Matron) its Chairman in her opening address at that time. The President was Miss F.R.Smith, Vice Presidents, Miss I. E. Dean and Miss C. M. Littlewood, Miss J. G. Shaw was Honorary Treasurer and the Executive Committee;

Miss J. Healey, Miss M. D. Griffiths, Mrs. P. F. Hobbs,

Miss H. Heyes, Miss M. McKenzie, Miss M. A. Margoschis,

Mrs J. Stokes and Miss M. E. Selman.

I had the pleasure of talking to members of the Nurses' League, on Saturday 10th, May 1997, their 33rd Anniversary. Miss P. M. Reed. M.B.E. a founder member and Honorary Secretary , being present, in her capacity of Past President).

Mr. Max Harrison's connection with the Robert Jones and Agnes Hunt Orthopaedic Hospital, Oswestry, in 1964, further strengthened the close bonds with the Woodlands, his attachment being on the basis of one attendance per month.

The C.S.S-C. have reviewed the Visiting Arrangements as at March 1965, as: Adult Ward, Woodlands,

Monday; Tuesday; Thursday; Friday; Saturday, 7.15pm - 8pm.

Wednesday 2pm. - 3pm. Sunday 2pm.- 3.30pm

Visitors are not required to produce a pass, but in the general interest only two are allowed at the bedside. Children up to 14 years may only visit the wards between 2 and 2.30 pm. on Sundays.

The arrangements for children's wards being that there are no fixed visiting hours, parents and adult relatives being welcome to visit the ward at any time except when the treatment or education of the child makes this impossible. Visiting cannot be allowed during the hospital school term between 10 and 12 am. and 1.30 and 3.30 pm. on weekdays. Visitors may be asked to leave during Consultants' ward-rounds . Children up to 14 can only be permitted to visit under exceptional circumstances at the discretion of the Ward Sister.

'You are requested not to smoke on the Wards'

1964 saw a number of important entries in committee minutes. A new potato peeler and fish fryer being installed in the main kitchen. The new oil-fire is proving most successful and saving over one hour daily of Domestic's time. Miss Shapland, the Head Mistress at Forelands, leaves after 30 years with the children both at Forelands and Woodlands in April 1965. Seven months later Miss Galbraith was admitted to the Queen Elizabeth Hospital. 21st December 1967 was a black day when the Forelands School was officially closed. Ward 4 was however to admit children under school age. Miss Kathy Kirby visited the patients, that year.

The Women's Voluntary Service were to take over the Buffet at Woodlands, as from February 8th 1965, opening as a canteen for patients' visitors to be opened at visiting times only. As from that date beverages and snacks previously served to staff were to be available in No. 3 Dining Room, which was to be developed as a non-resident staff canteen.

Two events occurring within but 3 months of each other in mid 1965, were the retirements of the Scoutmasters' at both Woodlands and Forelands, the former on the grounds of outside commitments, and the latter due to the difficulties in organising Scout activities with the introduction of unrestricted visiting.

A Programme for the new Physiotherapy School was well in hand:-

Sketch Plans	To be prepared and approval obtained January/April 1965.
Working Drawings	April/October 1965
Bills of Quantities	October/December 1965
Tender Period	January/March 1966
Contract Period	April/September 1966.

The programme allowing about three months for the completed building to be equipped and commissioned in time for it to be in operation when the lease of Belmont expires.

The Woodlands gardeners washing facilities were to be improved, by the proposal that a wash-hand basin was to be placed in the toilets at the rear of the Boiler House, currently being rebuilt. The 'bad news' being, that to facilitate access of vehicles collecting pig-swill and ashes, a small oak tree was to be removed.

The Committee were reminded, in 1966, that a scheme for the provision of a Chapel at Woodlands had been left in abeyance some years before. Agreeing to the Rev. Mr. Morton's concern the Committee however felt that a Chapel should be on a more modest scale than that originally envisaged. Attention was also given to the fact that there were still two toilets in the Nurses' Home without electric light. This was to be rectified as part of the scheme to upgrade the bathrooms, which also involved converting one of the rooms to a shampoo room. Senior Nursing Staff at Forelands were to be provided with kitchenette facilities.

The question of the Chapel arose again in March 1966, when it was decided that " ... in view of the need to make the best possible use of all accommodation, a purpose-built full-time Chapel should not be built. A compromise being that the present Buffet should be made available to the Chaplains' as an office and Room of Meditation for patients or relatives." The Chapel at Forelands had been inspected by the House Committee Visitors' and found to be in a serious state of dilapidation. It was recommended that in view of the extremely limited use now made of the Chapel, it should be demolished. The Forelands Chaplains agreed and an assurance was given that Services would continue, as at present, to be held on the wards.

There is trouble with the 'Time-Clock' at Woodlands, reported by the makers as being over 40 years old. It was continually in need of attention, and 'miss-clockings' were leading to difficulties in connection with wage payments. A replacement would cost about £100.

In 1967 the W.V.S. are looking to extending the opening-times of the Buffet at Woodlands to provide the service for patients and their relatives each morning. The patients' Buffet at Broad Street were also to receive the same services thanks to Mrs. E. Williams, organiser of the Hospital Canteens, indicating that her Organisation would be prepared to take over the Buffet. It would be open for more hours, than at present. Mrs. Mould who was at present in charge of the Buffet would be made responsible for Laundry and Linen arrangements in the Clinic and Physiotherapy Department.

Car parking at Woodlands was the priority in March 1968, the Hospital Management Committee recommending that the Hedge and Flower bed between the two main entrance gates be removed to provide additional parking. Miss C. Jones, Headmistress at the Woodlands School for 18 years resigned on the 31st December 1968. The H.M.C. were recommending that urgent consideration be given to the inadequate toilet facilities on Wards, 4, 5, 6, 7, 8, 9, and 10.

On the 15th. January 1969 Belmont was vacated and formally handed back to the Bournville Village Trust. With the 'South Birmingham Management Committee' due to come into being as from the 1st. April 1969, the Hospital Management Committee was seeking the views of members as to whether the House Committees' should be retained as part of that Body.

Staff Catering Facilities were under consideration as at February 1969 with the following statement " ... In view of the impending introduction of a 'Pay-as-you-Eat' meals service for resident staff, a suggestion has been made that the staff dining rooms at Woodlands be centralised in the dining room attached to the new School of Physiotherapy. The Catering Advisor to the Regional Board had inspected the facilities and had submitted a report showing that such a scheme would be entirely practicable, and would achieve considerable economy."

At the Special Meeting of the House Committee held mid August it was announced that " ... The H.M.C. had decided to disband the House Committees at the end of August 1969. There was general expression of regret at this decision, and a feeling that the abolition of House Committees was not in the best interest of the hospital ." Following the disbandment, a Visiting Panel of three Hospital Management Committee members were to be set up for each hospital, Mrs. M. B. Derrington, Mr. W. J. Higson and Dr. R. J. Stanley being the appointees' from this hospital. Non - H.M.C. members at present serving on House Committees were invited to participate. Mr. D. J. Wood, Mrs. Joyce Cadbury, Mrs. P. Jameson Evans, Mr. L. J. N. Fisher, Mrs. E. Hendry and Mr. E. Rudman taking up the offer. The H.M.C. also asked hospitals to consider the formation of some sort of Committee in order to co-ordinate the various forms of voluntary support.

(We have been here before exactly 20 years ago, when Mr. H. F. Harvey was talking of such a break-up, and of the forming of voluntary bodies).

At the close of the House Committee 'minutes' in August 1969 the following summary is given as to the forming and Co-ordination of Voluntary Support at the Royal Orthopaedic Hospital.

"Largely because of its voluntary hospital origin and background the hospital has, since the inception of the Health Service, continued to enjoy a great deal of voluntary support. Apart from the more usual forms of service which are to be found in most hospitals there are a considerable number of organisations and individuals who have demonstrated over the years a great loyalty and affection for the hospital ... It is certain that to attempt an amalgamation of these bodies into any sort of friends organisation would be disastrous and it has always been the policy to encourage each to function independently but in consultation with the Administrator who has reported as necessary to the House Committee".

"This volume of support together with legacies and money 'disclaimed' by the Minister in 1948 has resulted in substantial accumulation of free monies and at the present time the amount earmarked for the R.O.H. represents approximately 65% of the Special Services Account for the whole Group. In the past the House Management Committee has accepted that the House Committee with a knowledge of local conditions and in many cases of the origins of donations was particularly fitted to advise on the application of these funds. In this way expenditure has been confined to projects of most benefit to the hospital and most closely in accord with the wishes of the donors".

"These circumstances have tended to place on the House Committee certain responsibilities for which a rotating panel of visitors would be unsuitable. It is hoped, therefore, that the H.M.C. will be prepared to consider the establishment of, in addition to the visiting panel, a Special Services Committee for the Royal Orthopaedic Hospital."

A constitution was proposed with the Functions of an S.S.C. being the providing of a focal point in which the activities of the various voluntary agencies are co-ordinated, but not to act as an amalgamating committee, on which organisations or individuals are represented. To act as an advisory body to the H.M.C. To act as a host organisation. To stimulate an extension of voluntary support.

We have arrived at the start of another period of hospital re-management, the proposed re-siting and break-up of the Woodlands seems to have abated, (well at least for the next 20 years) and matters settled going into the 1970's. The next few years are to see the increased benefits of the contributions of voluntary organisations with major developments in hospital facilities, and of course the forming (at last) of the League of Friends.

Before continuing with that story, the time has now come for us, or rather past patients and staff of the Woodlands, Forelands, Broad Street, and even the Old Newhall Street hospital, to tell of their experiences and to give their 'Memories'.

Sooty proves the perfect beside tonic
copyright: Birmingham Post & Mail

Chapter 8

Your Memories

Mrs. Cherry Lawley, nee Griffiths, at 17 years of age, entered Woodlands for Orthopaedic nursing and Physiotherapy training living in at Belmont. (First year in the house, then in the stables). Remembers Miss Littlewood who was in charge, Miss Stiff and Miss Fletcher.

Rules were strict, In at 10 p.m.. 11o'clock for a late pass, 12 o'clock for a theatre pass. If you had a room on the ground floor, there would frequently be the 'late knock at the window, to let in the late comers.' Matron was strict, one Christmas about 1938 following a night duty, some girls took the following day off, Cherry went home. There was trouble when Matron found out, however Dame Elizabeth Cadbury calmed the troubled waters "by fighting our cause."

The girls worked a 12 hour day from 8 a.m. to 8 p.m. with a two hour break 10 till 12; 2 till 4 or 6 till 8. and their pay was 30/- a month. When there were air-raid warnings, Slit-trenches in the grounds of the adjacent home of Mr. and Mrs Laurence Cadbury, 'The Davids' in Hole Lane were used.

Forelands plays but a small part in her memories, when in her final year she, together with a friend, were sent there. That memory being of 'farmed out with the local undertaker.'

It was not until 21st February 1955 that Mrs Lawley returned to the Woodlands, working part-time, remaining there until her retirement in 1981. She recalls, Miss Wildblood, Nancy Drage, Mrs Stone, and in particular Mr. Scrase, a very clever diagnostic man - always on the ball - a complete gentleman. Miss Horsfall, Head of the School of Physiotherapy had been a fellow student with Cherry at Belmont. A clear memory was that the roof of the Physiotherapy Out-patient Department was being eaten by squirrels.

Mr. John (Jack) Carney, from Moseley. At about 8 years of age, in 1917, Jack was unable to walk other than on the toes on his right foot, his left foot was alright. Jack recalls only that "the humane man" had visited the house, and diagnosed the need for an operation. The only 'body' around at that time that was certainly in the field of such visiting (getting the contacts from the general public) was, as far as this history is aware, the Crippled Children's Union and it is therefore probable that that 'humane man' was Mr. Frank Mathews.

Jack's mother was left to her own devices to get hold of the necessary 'notes' to enable him to get such an operation. This meant going around factories particularly from some of the smaller local companies in Summer Lane. In 1917 he recalls going up to Newhall Street, and entering up a very wide staircase to a ward. There were two wards, one for men and above it one for boys. He was surprised to find himself put in the men's ward. There were some twelve beds in the ward, a Tamworth (pronounced Tammerth) Miner in the bed opposite to Jack.

Naughton Dunn was Jack's consultant, "He was a real Scot, and wore grey flannel trousers, and a typical Tweed jacket", but the lasting impression that left its mark on this 8 year old, was "his large white hands, which when placed on my leg were always cold." Jack was operated upon after 3 or 4 days, "there were no pain-killers, and I cried for 3 days and nights in my bed."

Jack remained in the hospital for some six months and has no recollection of any physiotherapy, but had on a plaster cast, with a hole in the side to allow access for re-dressing.

At the age of 12 he had to return for another operation. By 1924 he was an orphan. In connection with the Crippled Children's Union he recalls his mother going to the C.C.U. offices then at Daimler House, Paradise Street, for assistance in obtaining 'notes', also to get 'Malt Extract' that was considered necessary for his welfare. He also received an invitation each year to the Christmas Party (put on by Edward Ansell) for crippled children at the Town Hall, and of course the visits to the Manor Farm by invitation of Mr. & Mrs George Cadbury, organised by the C.C.U. There was always a Punch and Judy show and plenty to eat.

Bobby Jones from Aston was but a few months old when first admitted to the Cripples Hospital in 1928, with very serious deformities to both of his legs, he was unable to walk. He was to be in the hospital on and off for ten years, during which time he had some 16 operations. He never attended the local infant school, but had all his education in the hospital school. "I could read by the time I was 4 years old, thanks to Nurse Pratt, (or Platt), this was part of 'Good nursing' "

Visiting was restricted to once every 3 months and later 2 months. Bobby took a dislike to the infrequent visits home, and was eager to return to hospital; fired by the ridicule he had to face when being pushed in a pram, from his peer group, especially as he grew older, " whereas in hospital I was amongst friends." He was repeatedly having to learn to walk again after each operation. and in the early days was completely strapped in a stretcher and unable to move.

Bobby was kept in contact with the out-side world by receiving Post cards. one of which was sent to his home, dated August 16, 1933, by J. Bent, a nurse at the outpatient department, Broad Street, (who subsequently married Mr. Donovan), and two to 'Master Bobby Jones, Ward 5' in August and September, 1935, from Miss Wilson, who was the Headmistress of Twickenham Road School, at which he had been registered by his mother; each carrying simple messages:- "This is just to send you our love & hope you are getting better" and "Miss Burton & I were so glad that you were in hospital at last & we shall be so glad to hear you are growing strong again. We do miss our big children. Love from Miss Wilson."

He grew up never feeling part of a family.

He admits to being a naughty boy. On one occasion he decided to make a break for it, and, somehow, walked out of the hospital and got onto a Tram-car to go home, not even knowing how to get there. Clearly the tram conductor had other ideas.

Mr. Wilson Stuart was his consultant surgeon.

Life in the Woodlands was a very strict regime, and not a relaxed one to live in. Bobby was interested when a scout troop affiliation with a local group was made at Woodlands. A constant worry for children was the possibility of continuous stays of up to six months at Woodlands, and, because of the then extreme difficulties for visitors travelling such a distance out of the city, being transferred to the Forelands, Bromsgrove.

In the "Cutting Edge" Newsletter of the Royal Orthopaedic Hospital NHS Trust and the League of Friends, for Winter 1995/96, readers were "Introduced to Our Chairman". Those readers will know of course that this article has been provided by:-

"Our Chairman" who was of course " young Master Bobby Jones."

Thank you Bob.

Mrs Alice Nichols, nee Betts, born in 1911 in Northfield. She attended St. Laurence's Church, and the Friends Institute (Church Road). An annual Anniversary, was held over three consecutive Sundays, in the July period. The third was the visit of the children to the Woodlands. During the preceding week, supported by adults, they visited all of the families around Northfield and collected eggs and any other groceries. This was 'Egg Sunday', and after dinner a large group of children lined up three abreast, with the front three children carrying large baskets full of the goodies. From the Institute this group, headed by a Brass Band, snaked its way up Church Road, turning right into Bristol Road South and down to the Cripple's Hospital, congregating in the courtyard. The patients were wheeled out onto the balconies, and the baskets having been passed to the Matron or nurses, they were treated to typical anniversary songs and hymns. Mr. and Mrs Parsons were the well loved and respected organisers of this event.

Mrs. Jean Lynch, nee Wallace, from Kings Norton, when about eleven years of age in 1942, had a paper round from Nixon's Newsagent situated in Bristol Road South, Northfield, that round was 'the Woodlands' where she delivered morning and evening papers, comics, magazines etc.. The older patients ordered 'snuff' for which Jean would take the orders in the morning and, herself, make up into 2 oz. cone-shaped packets to take in at night. Conveniently, for Jean, the local bread delivery man called in at the shop each morning, so enabling her to have a lift down to the Woodlands, on his horse-drawn cart.

She really made a hit in the men's cloister ward, when she offered to take in a packet of 'fish and chips'. It was not long before the orders were rolling in. How she brought, at one-time, some fifteen portions into the hospital,

The Courtyard and Balcony at Woodlands
Source: Royal Cripples Hospital, Annual Reports, 1925-1929
photo: Brian Jones

The Courtyard 1997
photo: Brian Jones

(at the chagrin of other customers in the shop, as it would mean them waiting for a new pan to be cooked,) without comment from the hospital staff, let alone the smell, amazed her., but there was never any comment. The conductor on the tram-car from Northfield to the hospital, did stipulate one condition, she had to go on the top deck.

Jean states that life at the Woodlands was one of happiness, with great friendliness throughout the establishment.

Mrs Hilda Mearden, Shenley Field Road,was in the Woodlands Hospital for some seven weeks in 1970, at the age of 51. having had a spinal operation. Her consultant surgeon being Mr. Leather. She had had back trouble from a child; and had taken a fall from a horse when in her early twenties; and at that period simply 'rested up' at home in bed.

Mrs Mearden having completely 'locked' when stooping in order to carry out some housework, in September 1970, reported to the Woodlands by her own doctor, was visited by Mr. Cotterill, severe lower spinal deformity apparently being the cause, and immediately taken in to the hospital. On entering she was most pleasantly surprised to find that two of the trainee doctors there, were former school friends of her son. Memories of her relatively brief stay, was the marvellous and friendly attention provided by all the staff, and she was always impressed with the tidiness and standard of the nurses' uniforms, which made them much respected.

Mr. Robert Christie, Tyburn Road. born 1907. As a lad, and later as the Goal Keeper for the Work's football team he was very active and would have of course suffered numerous accidents, it was not however until September 1939, that he went to the Out-patient Department at Broad Street. An initial examination of his spine gave, as he thought, no concern. He returned home and was surprised, only some two days later, to be ordered back immediately to Broad Street.

He was examined by Mr. Leather (a wonderful man). After two or three days he was sent to the Royal Cripples' Hospital, (the Woodlands) surprisingly having to make his own way there. No operation was performed, but he was measured for a spinal frame, and a plaster case built up on the front of his body. The spinal frame made from steel rod, was designed to the shape of his legs with foot plates, suitably padded and bandaged, and up to his neck the back support, with another plate, behind his neck and above his head, which carried a mirror. For two and a half years he lay flat on his back, able only to look upwards, using the mirror to see his food placed in a convenient position on his chest, so enabling him to feed himself, and see around him, the steel frame was protected with leather. Leather straps and bandages went across his legs and body, and cotton wool padding placed under the knees. He regularly suffered not only from soreness, but even raw hips and back, going right down to the bone. Here the front body-cast came into use, when every two or three weeks he was turned over and placed front down into that cast for a few days.

At the end of two and a half years he came out of the frame, and simply could not walk; completely stiff he was given massage and physiotherapy. Miss Wildblood; Miss Kerr and Miss Robinson being amongst the nurses for whom he had so much praise. The surgeons, in addition to Mr. Leather; were Pop Stuart and Mr. F.G.Allen. Add to these the Head Porter Ted Corrie, who would on a Monday morning come through the ward with the tray of knives for the operating theatre, saying "come on then I'm ready for you.",

It took some three to four months to learn to walk. For seven years he needed to wear a specially reinforced jacket. Returning home was in itself a strange experience, if not only for the reason that his son, born whilst he was in hospital, did not know him.

Mr. Ivor Cooke, Hole Lane, Northfield. writes; my family lived in Hole Farm from about 1890 until my Aunt died in 1964. The Woodlands was just across the fields from the farm and my grandparents rented the farm from Mr. Abraham who lived at the Woodlands. When he died they bid against the Cadbury family and bought the farm and two large meadows. (Mr. Cooke's cottage was built, in 1905, in one of those meadows). He so kindly has given me access to the brochure on which the sale of the house (Woodlands) and land at the Woodlands,and all Mr. Abraham's other property is set out.

Ivor was born at the Davids cottage, almost opposite to Belmont. He possesses a medal from "The Cripples Hospital", the reward for donating small (very small !) sums from my pocket money to the hospital in the

1920s. The highlight of the year in Hole Lane was the annual fundraising fete at the Woodlands, complete with roundabouts etc. and followed by a fireworks display. The Davids House was the property of Mr. & Mrs Laurence Cadbury from 1924, and the medal carries the name 'Band of Help' which was the school children's money raising effort.

The following, very simple note from Mrs Rosie E. Morton (nee Butler) of Great Barr, speaks volumes:-

I want to say I owe my whole life to the Wonderful Hospital the *Woodlands Orthopaedic. I had a very serious operation on my leg when I was about 8 years old, which enabled me to walk properly. I am now 95 years old and still able to walk I hope for a long time yet if the Lord will spare me. *Young Rosie would have been treated at what was then the Crippled Children's Hospital.

A very deep and sincere appreciation of "The Angel of Mercy" a physiotherapist at the Cripple's Hospital, comes from Mr. Basil Walker from Handsworth Wood.

"I personally feel that no history of the Royal Orthopaedic Hospital would be complete without mentioning the Angel of Mercy."

Basil enclosed an appreciation of her:-

Miss Lund Physiotherapist - Extraordinary

I first came into the caring hands of Miss Lund at the Cripples Hospital, Broad Street in the latter half of the 1920's. She worked very hard to alleviate for me and other members of the family, a congenital complaint that we have. I was to be under her care throughout the 30's and have benefited ever since.

To me as a very small child, she at first appeared awesome, a disciplinarian of the first order, but as time passed I began to appreciate more and more the love she put into the work that she was doing, and which spilled over to include the people for whom she cared. This took her into the world of the slums, yard's with their single water taps, depression, poverty, privation etc., she took a breath of fresh air.. How many empty bellies were filled from her purse !

Mrs Doreen M. Brownhill, nee Mansell, from Marston Green. relates a few memories during her fifteen months as a patient in 'The Woodlands' Orthopaedic Hospital.

I contracted Polio in August 1952 and was admitted to Little Bromwich Isolation Hospital and spent my 21st Birthday there. I was then transferred to the Woodlands. As I gradually recovered my paralysed limbs a Mr. Donovan came to see me and assess what little movement I had in the early stages. I was transferred to Woodlands at the end of October 1952, and Mr. Donovan promised that he would get me mobile with the aid of callipers, physiotherapy and weekly exercise in the hydrotherapy pool. Eventually my spine became strong enough to support my body without a back support so with the aid of under-arm crutches I was able to take a few steps. My physiotherapist was a Miss Dorothy Head and the Head of the department was a Miss Wildblood.

I had to spend Christmas in hospital and everyone made life as enjoyable as possible starting with a candlelight procession singing carols by the light of the lanterns, visiting each ward (not a dry eye in the house). Mr. Scrase the Senior House Surgeon, carved the Turkey.

For a look at the organisation outside of the hospitals, for the raising of funds, Mrs N. Playdon of Worlds End Lane, Quinton offers the following recollections from her childhood:

A Great Aunt of mine was a barmaid and later on in charge of the Grill Room at the Waterloo Hotel in Waterloo Road, Smethwick. Once a year a fruit and vegetable show was held there and she was always involved. The proceeds were donated to the Woodlands for the upkeep of a bed or beds.

Many of the contributors to this chapter have echoed the words 'The Woodlands was their second home'. Mrs M. Gould, from West Bromwich, recalls:

I joined Woodlands in January 1950 as a very raw 16 year old, to do two years nursing before going on to general training; little did I realise it was to shape the rest of my life. Many of the patients in those years were either polio victims or suffering from T. B. bones, the treatment for the latter being, the then new drug streptomycin, fresh air and immobilisation for very long periods. Woodlands became their second home. On Saturdays

203

relatives could bring in plates of homemade food, which the nurses were required to warm up (no microwaves then) and serve to the respective patients, heaven help us if they got the wrong one. There were radios and also gramophones on the lockers, along with the water jugs which would be frozen solid in the winter.

You cannot possibly write about the Royal Orthopaedic Hospital without mentioning Wilson Stuart, writes Miss M. Owen from Sheldon, he was a great surgeon and considerate man, especially with children. I was in the Woodlands in 1924 as a child of 5 years old and had an operation on my leg, but there wasn't any pre-med, you were wheeled straight into the operating theatre and the doctors and nurses were already robed up, with their masks on which was very frightening to a child. A number of children had to lie on their backs on frames, as I did for a month, but we had some happy times. Your parents were only allowed to visit once a month.

The wards were open all down one side and the nurses used to push us out on to the verandah in our beds when it was sunny. One time I had both feet in plaster and I remember the nurse tying them both up to the taps in the bath so the plasters didn't get wet.

Mr. Ronald Glover writing from New Oscott relives his early days in the Woodlands and Forelands during the late twenties and early thirties :- Although very young I remember the open ward in the Woodlands where the complete wall on one-side would be open to the elements. Recollections of visiting day (once a week) and the anticipation of seeing my parents walking along the ward, and wondering what small toy they were bringing me this week. This must have been an enormous struggle with a journey from Kingstanding by bus and tram.

I remember Christmas in the children's ward and the day trips out from the Forelands. Many other memories come flooding back, like the time I was moved away from the window because I was able to gather snow from the outer sill and snowball the other children. Going to the operating theatre and waking up to find my body and left leg encased in plaster, and later the feel of the shears as they cut the plaster case away.

Life in the hospital was the norm for me until I was about 6 to 7 years old, and afterwards there was the visits to Broad Street, as an outpatient where one recalls long waits in the waiting room to see a doctor or to be fitted with an iron, or special shoes. The place always seemed to be filled with crippled children, and most of the administrative staff also seemed to be crippled in some way. The Cripples Hospital must have done wonderful work in those days, because I'm 70 now and still going strong.

The next letter is, at times, a real tear-jerker. from:-

Mr. N. H. Field, from Harborne. I spent several years in treatment at the Woodlands mainly as a child, for spinal T. B. being admitted in 1921. (he recalls the surgeon at that time, as Naughton Dunn). There were no drugs for T. B. in those days, so, after an initial operation I was immobilised on a spinal frame for about six years, I was then 3 years old. At the age of 8 or 9 years, I was got back on my feet and began learning to walk again. Unfortunately on my second day up, I fell over backwards and broke a leg. This caused some delay, but eventually I was moved to the Forelands to recover in what was then an open-air country retreat in beautiful green surroundings, and for the first time I realised I had been through Hell and had now arrived in Paradise.

This was the first of two periods I spent at Forelands, and the first happiness I had ever known in childhood, having lost both father and mother, before and during my illness-to the same dreadful disease for which at that time there was no cure. My time at Woodlands was mostly a blur with just a few highlights such as the frequent visits to the wards of Dame Elizabeth Cadbury, also the visit of the then Prince of Wales, later Edward V111. when all the patients on frames or in plaster, where possible, were carried out and laid in line along the front wall, 'like a row of exhibits' for The Prince's inspection. I was one of these.

My memories of Forelands are more intense, and very much happier, sleeping in wards wide open on one side, summer or winter, with views across miles of beautiful country all the way up to the Malverns; the beautiful big house with panelled Dining Hall where we had our meals-Harvey, the Hospital's horse, taking us in the pony-trap for picnics at Grafton Manor - the excitement of the Christmas play - snow blowing into the open wards in winter - lazing on a green lawn under the pine-trees on a hot summer afternoon,: a wonderfully happy time, until it was discovered that my lungs were affected by the T.B. and I was shoved into an ambulance and sent without any warning to Yardley Sanatorium. In those days the last to be told anything about himself was the patient so when I got there and found myself in a closed ward full of really sick kids, some of them dying, I was utterly terrified, thinking I must have done something wicked, to be thrown out of my paradise, without explanation, and into what seemed like Hell, with children suffering, moaning all night, then being dead in the morning.

After some months of this, I eventually became well enough to move to an open ward, which was rather better, being what I'd been used to. The Sanatorium episode lasted some 9 or 10 months, then for the first time since I was three, I was sent home, a completely strange environment, where there was no grass, no trees, and no proper flowers, and I soon hated it, and began to get ill again. This turned out to be all to the good, for after visits to the Broad Street Clinic I was sent for another stay at the Forelands. Almost immediately I settled back into the Spartan routine as before, as though I hadn't been away. Most, perhaps all of my old fellow-patients had been replaced by others, yet somehow they were the same boys' with different names and I was back with my old chums in the only place I wanted to be. This time I was at Forelands for about a year, another Christmas, another wonderful summer.

Mr. Michael G. Lee, from Hollywood had experiences of the Children's Hospital, Forelands and Woodlands:- I entered the Woodlands at the age of 8½ years, in 1945, and diagnosed with a T. B. spine, and put into a small isolation ward in the Children's Hospital, Ladywood. From there after some 4 weeks I was moved to the Woodlands for assessment under the care of a wonderful surgeon Mr. F. G. Allen. The only treatment for T. B. spines, or hips, was a very long rest on a Thompson frame which kept the body and legs completely immobile for a minimum of 18 months to 2 years. In view of the fact that I did not need surgery I was moved to the Forelands Hospital, before Christmas 1945.

During the next 2½ years my stay in the hospital was very happy, the nurses were very young, 16 +, and very dedicated. We were very cold in bed in winter, and quite hot in summer. We had full education, and the highlight of the week was the visit by TOC. H. who brought movie films, full-feature or shorts, with ginger beer and chocolate. There was no T.V. in those days our saviour being the wireless, listening for hours to football and cricket matches; the days of Bradman; Hutton; Compton; Edrich. The Manchester United F. A. Cup winning team visited us in 1948. We also had a piece of the Queen's Wedding cake. Looking back to those years in hospital, it was all about wonderful nursing, patience and a lot of luck.

Mrs M.J.Hinton, Leamore, Walsall, had 3 operations as a baby at Broad Street 1927 - 28, for 2 badly deformed club feet, by Mr. Leather. When 11 years old I was sent to the clinic to see Mr. Mills, who operated at the Woodlands, in May 1938. I remember being in the long ward open all down one side, this was never closed. The one high spot was when the Taxi Drivers took all who could be carried to Tewkesbury for the day, we had tea and cakes at the side of the river it was wonderful. But the moment that sticks in my mind was when my bed was named by Dame Elizabeth Cadbury, the Press were there and I was quite a celebrity for half an hour of my young life.

I also remember we had a Fete and my Sunday School Teacher brought my mother, but she was not allowed to visit me and could only shout across from a barrier, which I thought terrible at the time.

Mrs. Evelyn.A.Cooksey, nee Allen, from Walmley, Sutton Coldfield. born 1910, recalls Egg-Sundays during the period 1920-30. and the Northfield Friends Institute. My sister and I always collected in West Heath Road, we usually finished with a 100+.

When I was 16 I joined the Northfield Ranger Guide Company. Our special duty was to take our 'Promise' into a Wider World - thus 'service'. To this end three of us spent our Friday evenings at the Woodlands, sewing buttons and tapes on gowns used in the operating theatre. One night a nurse suggested we visit the children. They loved to see us in our Guide uniforms. Subsequently the sewing night became Guide Company night in the ward & when I was 18 years old I was made Acting Captain of the Guide Company we had formed.

The Guides were provided with uniforms, just to the waist as they were in beds. We pulled the beds into a circle in the ward, put a mock fire (red paper, sticks and a torch) on a locker, dimmed the lights & sang campfire songs. We were allowed to take them to Church Parade at Kings Norton Church.

Mr. and Mrs Crooks from Kings Heath, Eric and Peggy nee Geens, were both connected with Scouts and Guides as children. In 1937-38 Eric was a Wolf Cub with the 1st Masshouse Scout Group (Cotteridge) and used to go along to the Woodlands and play games. The boys at Woodlands were themselves in uniform, he recalls, so there must have been an existing Cub Pack.

Peggy went from her Cotteridge Guide Company during 1944-45 to help at the Woodlands doing washing up and tidying in the wards. I often went home upset after seeing young soldiers who had lost their limbs. My father threatened to stop me going but I thought it was important to keep going.

Mrs. Dorothy Ellis, from Solihull, writes:-

I trained as an orthopaedic nurse from August 1944 until August 1947. In 1950 I joined the Outpatient Department at Broad Street until the birth of my first child in 1952. and returned there in 1963 remaining until 1976. in those years great changes took place. In the early days we had five consultants who worked in the mornings. In the afternoon sessions we did remedial work - a great deal of splint making in plaster of paris. ... We had three workshops - a metal shop, boot department and splint department. Most of the workers were ex-patients, many polio or T.B. patients. They had been through the hospital school, and missed a great deal of schooling, and were therefore in safe, if not well paid, employment and were excellent caring workers.

In later years when T.B. and polio had largely been eradicated there was a change in the conditions we treated - total hip replacements, knee replacements and then other smaller joints - even finger joints for patients with rheumatoid arthritis. We had special clinics for babies with club foot deformities, spinal curvature, hand conditions, along with all the other orthopaedic problems concerned with joints and bones and muscles. Many of the staff served the hospital for much of their working lives, and were devoted to it. I always felt that the Woodlands and Broad Street were like a big family.

Mrs. Shelagh Eglinton, nee Reed, Tidbury Green, Solihull. recalls her late sister Kathleen's treatment, in the Woodlands 1937-39.

I remember seeing snow on Kathleen's bed in Ward 4, the open-air ward. Kay had lessons in the school at the Woodlands, and then went back to her Grammar School to take Higher School Certificate and thence to college, so the lessons were good. Mr. Leather disproved the doctor's verdict of "never walk again", Kay walked, danced, married and had a daughter. My father was allowed to take Kay and a friend out for a ride in the car at weekends, Luckily he was in the 'Birmingham Saturday Hospital Fund' otherwise the costs would have pauperised him. Both had huge plasters on their legs and had to be carried to the car. Shelagh joined one such trip "it was a squeeze, with mother as well" but the trip to the 'Fleur de Lys' at Lowsonford, to sit by the canal, with a cheese and bread meal (before the days of the famous Pies), on a lovely sunny day was a very enjoyable one away from the hospital.

Mrs. Kathleen Pitman, from Smethwick, as a 51/2 year old in 1925 became a patient at Smethwick Cripples Union. Treated for 'flu', but later it became apparent that it was polio as she developed Infantile paralysis, affecting the right foot.

Mr. Wilson Stuart saw me at the clinic and for seven years I received treatment and wore an iron brace up to my knee. The staff of the C.U. were Miss Jenkins, secretary, Miss Reeves who I think was clerk and the three therapists, Misses Williams, Grey and Little. In 1932 Mr. Stuart operated on my foot and I was at Woodlands for three weeks. The operation was very successful! After about a year I was able to be without the iron and wear low shoes instead of boots.

The staff of Ward 4 where I was were, Staff Nurse Perkins, and Nurses Thomas, Keen and Bailey. We had some schooling, two teachers came to the ward, I remember doing some arithmetic and embroidery. It was a girls ward, ages from about 5 - 16. Some of us were taken in cars for an outing to Holt Fleet and to the gardens of the Cadbury Manor House.

I think the R.O.H. has always been a wonderful hospital, having a friendly atmosphere and dedicated staff.

Mrs. Edna Dawson, nee Kendrick, (a spritely 85 years of age) from

Handsworth Wood, at the age of 11 years entered the Newhall Street, Cripple's Union Hospital. Major Naughton Dunn operated on her amputating her left foot. "He gave me a sixpenny piece for being so good".

The only heating was from coal-fires; there was no Lift. It took some eleven months for Edna to learn to walk again, with her artificial foot strapped on. She soon however found herself able to take part in all the normal play activities of her friends. The cost of the treatment was covered thanks to her father being a Tram Driver with the Birmingham Corporation, so automatically covered by the Saturday Hospital Fund. During her months at home she was frequently visited by Mr. Frank Mathews with his motor bike and side car.

Edna in looking around for some form of hospital job, made contact in 1933 with Fanny Smith, whom she had known at Newhall Street. Matron Smith arranged for an appointment for a vacancy at the Forelands, and for four years, 1933 to 1937, Edna worked on the telephone switchboard, so coming into contact with the consultants of the day, Wilson Stuart; Leather and Mills. Part of her time was spent involved in the recovering of frames and saddles, 'I spent a month learning the leather work at Broad Street, before taking up the Forelands post', also the teaching of sewing to the children. "The education was wonderful". Miss Edwards was the Head mistress and there were two other teachers, who did not live in. Matron Lamb at Forelands, and Sister Riley stand out in her memory, as do Mr. & Mrs Weaver who lived at the Lodge, he being the Head gardener.

Questioned as to her memories of 'Harvey' the horse, Edna sadly recollected that, unexpectedly, she was present when the ageing animal ("he came with the house") was put to sleep.

Edna Kendrick was 'giving back' to the hospital for what it had done for her as a child, little thinking that she would shortly be returning again as a patient. Buried under the rubble of the families bombed home in Newtown, in 1941, she was found to have a splintered Fibular in that same left leg. X-rayed at Forelands, she was then examined by Mr. Wilson Stuart at Broad Street. His diagnosis was not good, and she was offered a choice, "I cannot guarantee successful surgery, and would advise the amputation of the leg, below the knee". With the confidence of previous experience, she had no doubt as to the correct step to take. Edna was now given a complete lower leg and foot. Edna's only satisfaction was that " It cost nothing, because it was due to the war ". She then spent seven weeks in the Woodlands.

Mrs. Edith Crow, Kings Heath, and her daughter Mrs. Linda Moss, most kindly guided me through a photograph album, which specifically related to Edith's aunt, the late Mrs. Beatrice Mary Hill, nee' Thomas. Beatrice would have been known as Nurse Thomas, from the time of her commencing her duties at the Woodlands in 1920, as a student Radiographer, until her marriage to Alf Hill, (whom she met through the Woodlands Car Club) on November 16th, 1941. Later as Sister Hill subsequently becoming Superintendent of the Radiology department. At her retirement on the 9th November, 1957 she received a framed, testimonial " 'The Hospital Management Committee on your retirement from the Hospital service desire to place on record your 37 years of public service, and to express their appreciation of the loyal and efficient manner in which you have performed the duties entrusted to you."

There is nothing special in such a recognition, but behind it lies an interesting past:- Beatrice born in 1898 in Stirchley, became a patient at the Woodlands when, at 18 years of age, she had a leg amputated below the knee. Whilst recovering she used to help around the wards, and, as Edith then says, "she never came home". So enthralled with the hospital atmosphere she stayed on. "Fanny Smith (Matron) was her home". Beatrice wrote the following letter re-her Wedding Day, which indicates the great respect and affection with which she was held as a nurse, by the medical staff:-

A Day to Remember - My Wedding Day 16th November 1940

"During the days of the air-raids over Birmingham I was living at Woodlands Hospital. On the 15th November bombs were dropped over Birmingham. My wedding dress was under the rubble in Birmingham; but members of the staff rallied around to get me another dress, and get me to the church. Our Radiologist who was to give me away was held up at another Hospital, as there were so many casualties he could not get away, eventually he arrived, still dressed in his theatre garb, with overcoat on

211

top. I was duly married, and had a wonderful reception in the Hospital."
(That Radiologist was no less a personage than the eminent Dr. James
Brailsford). Beatrice continues:-

On the following Friday Evening I was sitting with the two Night Sisters,
I had to leave them, and only twenty minutes later a Bomb was dropped on
the Hospital, and they were both killed.

Edith Crow also gave an interesting fact. Her father born with deformed
feet, in 1880, at barely an hour old was taken immediately to the Old
General Hospital, (which stood in Summer Lane) for the necessary surgery.

Memories of Broad Street, 1942 - 45. At first, in the mornings, I helped
Miss Ella Jones; writes Mary Bowers of Edgbaston; with the "crippled"
pupils to whom we taught shorthand and typing. There were about eight
young people and the schoolroom was adjacent to the large waiting hall.

In the afternoons I worked in the Appeals Office with Miss May Cooke.
She used to visit schools in the Midlands to give talks about "The Royal
Cripples Hospital" and to receive money which the pupils had collected.
(this would probably have been the 'band of Help'). As she was unable to
drive (she only had a short stump of a left arm) I used to take her around
in the hospital car - an Austin 7 as I recall. We ran an appeal, in which
collecting cards were sent out to former patients who collected donations
from friends and relations. They were generous. But I do remember a
couple of amusing replies with cards returned empty - "As I have recently
been a guest of His Majesty's prison I don't think I had better collect this
year." Another read "Bill Jones has died - all communications ceased."

Later I became a Clinic Stenographer. (Nothing as grand as medical
secretaries those days) Clinics actually began soon after 9 a.m. but patients
would be there more than an hour beforehand in the hope of being seen
early so that they could get back to work. They sat patiently on long
benches (no timed appointments then). Sometimes it was 3 p.m. when the
clinic finished.

The following adds a little bit of information, not previously highlighted
' the record card colour system.'

Consultants were :

Monday - Mr. Wilson Stuart   -   blue record card
Tuesday - Mr. F.G.Allan   -   yellow record card
Wednesday - Mr. J.B.Leather   -   pink record card
Thursday - Mr. A.M.Hendry   -   fawn record card
Friday - Mr. Percival Mills   -   white record card

No clinic on Saturdays, but we worked 9 a.m. till 12 noon on three Saturdays out of four.

As a stenographer one accompanied the surgeon as he examined each patient, took down the examination notes in shorthand, the letter to the G.P. and wrote out in long-hand on a chit the treatment recommended, X-rays to be taken etc. One had to be equipped with a tendon hammer and tape measure, and was sometimes expected to carry wooden blocks for measuring leg shortening and at times had wet X-rays in frames hanging from one's fingers. All this was done walking round the clinic, in and out of the curtained cubicles.

Clinic stenographers, cash room staff, and registration office staff all wore green overalls. In the dining room we sat on one long table, and the white overall massage girls and nurses sat at the other table. It was not "done" to mix. I think it was Easter 1944 when The Chartered Society of Massage and Medical Gymnasts held their Annual Meeting in Birmingham and changed their title to The Chartered Society of Physiotherapists.

We did fire-watching duty, and slept on some form of stretcher. The girl on duty with me was more afraid of cockroaches than bombs, so insisted on sleeping on top of the tables in the cash office. In the morning I recall frying bacon in the plaster room at the end of the clinic.

It was a very friendly hospital. Many of the staff were disabled.

Miss Deirdre Hodgson, NCSP. of Hall Green adds to the air-raid warning activity. Dee' having joined the staff of the, then, Royal Cripple's Hospital, in September 1940 as Educational Gymnast in the then Massage Department at Broad Street, being in sole charge of the Gym. Air raids were an everyday part of life. A Firewatching rota every eighth night was hair-raising but could be amusing "Soon after my arrival at Broad Street Miss Wild from the Finance Staff came up to the Gym to ask what I would like for supper. She suggested 'pork pie and tomato'. I was happy to agree which was just as well as there was never anything else." Another incident remembered was the night that the Prince of Wales Theatre in Broad Street was bombed. (9th April 1941), "It felt as if the hospital had been blown up. We all went out, as per instructions, into the car-park wearing our tin hats. Our team being augmented by a member of the Friends Ambulance Unit (A Society of Friends organisation), and he was mesmerised by seeing Gwen Lister (one of our team) who was wearing her curlers under her tin hat. As soon as the 'All Clear' went, we had to sweep up all the Shrapnel which had been raining down and had been bouncing off our tin hats as we watched for incendiaries".

Remaining there until 1950, Dee' who had been trained as a Physical Education Teacher and Masseuse at the Bergman Osterberg PE. College in Dartford, Kent, 1937 - 40, moved for 10 years to Warwick Hospital returning to Broad Street in 1960, remaining there till retirement in 1984. "I was very sorry to retire and missed my work very much".

Mrs. Hilda Taylor, nee Wild, from Erdington (the purveyor of Dee's pork-pie and tomato, and still Dee' Hodgson's close friend), writes of having joined the Finance Staff in November 1930. Discipline was strict even for Clerical Staff, overalls of different colours were worn by all girls showing their grade. For 2 days every summer a Fete was held in the fields at Woodlands, all members of the inpatient and outpatient staff having to work hard on the various stalls. A V.I.P. would open the Fete on the Friday and Hilda remembers Helen Pickard. wife of Cedric Hardwick, Cora Giffon and Emile Littler, (he had been invited to join the Board of the Prince of Wales Theatre in 1935), also Lady Throckmorton and Ronald Cartland, MP. brother of Barbara Cartland. The memory of Dame Elizabeth Cadbury riding on the Carousel at a Fete when in her eighties, is strong. "Again, all staff members were expected to sell Flags in the City - saying 'Please help the Cripples', but when we changed to the Royal Orthopaedic (1949) the last word was taboo".

Mrs. D.M.Darby from Pype Hayes was 'one of two housemaids' at Belmont in the 1930s. There was also the cook and her husband who was the gardener, and a kitchen maid.

My remembrance of the Hospital began when I was about 3 years old, writes Mrs. A. Greaves of Kitts Green, now in her seventies, my grandfather told my father to take me to have my legs looked at as I was knock-kneed. I had my legs broken and set at the Woodlands, I then had to wear irons up to my thighs. I also went to Forelands. I went to a Cripple's School in Little Green Lane until I was ten and a half years old, in between going for exercises at Broad Street. I remember the Doctor's name Mr. Stuart. I was quite a tom-boy in those days and wanted to do as the other children did, stand on my hands. I broke my Irons many times.

The trams running past the Woodlands, to the Lickey Hills, at the time of 'George V ' Jubilee, mark the start of the memories of Mr. W. A. Skidmore, of Smethwick. That being the occasion when the children were given Jubilee Celebration cups each with an egg inside. He recalls the courtyard with its fish pond, to the left of which, was the plaster room with plaster casts of bodies. When he was being fitted 'with plaster from under my arms and down my left leg to the ankle, I lay on the table, with a biscuit tin under my head, my legs were separated by a peg, enabling the nurses to apply the plaster.' After which he had to go for two days under a Dryer, like a big tunnel with Electric lights either side.

At Christmas the wards were decorated, each with a different theme, there being a competition for the best decoration, and a surgeon used to carve the Turkey on each ward. Mr. Skidmore remembers finding toys at the bottom of the beds on Christmas morning, and seeing Dame Elizabeth Cadbury coming around on numerous occasions with gifts. Visiting was allowed on a fortnightly Sunday basis only, for 2 hours. Entertainment included a Fair, when mobile children could be taken around by their parents, and a Visiting Circus on the Green in front of Ward 5. "I remember when a Clown on stilts came to me and I cried."

War-time memories remain, patients' being issued with Enamel Bowls and Blankets to cover their heads from flying glass as they couldn't get the beds away from windows quick enough. Sadly he recalls the death of the two Night Sisters. Following that attack Mr. Skidmore was one of those transferred to Forelands. The doctors from Woodlands, Mr. Wilson Stuart, Dr. Leather, Dr. Donovan, visited them each week.

Life at Forelands brings back many memories. Matron was Sister Pocock and the Nurses, still remembered were Fay, Henderson and J. Walker. Two of his teachers were, N. Shepland, who taught handicraft, and, whilst lying on the frame on his back he made a foot stool which he still has in his possession. Miss M. Moore taught Music, and how to sing. There were two Scoutmasters' Mr. Harding and Mr. Swinnerton. They taught us Morse Code and Semaphore and basic scouting. The beds being pushed into a field where there was a tent. They also had camp-fires. The field looked on to the 'Lickey Incline' so we could see the trains going up the hill. A Donkey and Cart was used to take patients to Church in Bromsgrove on Sunday Mornings.

Open-Air conditions existed both at Forelands and Woodlands, when "... we were left out on concrete slabs outside the Ward in all weathers, covered by a water proof sheet put over the bedding."

Another frightening war-time experience was when young Master Skidmore observed an aircraft flying so low that it had to turn sideways to get through the trees. An event just as scaring for the nurses as they lay on the ground.

Mrs. Margaret Handley of Kings Norton, one of the current Vice Presidents of the League of Nurses & Physiotherapists, was at the Woodlands from September 3rd 1939 to November 30th 1944, undertaking her training for Orthopaedic and Physiotherapy nursing. Margaret has added information to that previously stated by the Matron Fanny Smith in her report of the bombing.

It was Sunday afternoon visiting time - the first visit since the bombing. In those days it was visiting on Wednesdays and Sundays only. I was on Cloister and Ward 6, when the men said "No Visitors", they were not going to have visitors without having a shave, and we had no water, only a few gallons of drinking water in the kitchen. On Cloister we had some walking soldiers and so some of them broke the ice in the pond in the court-yard, and took every man half a shaving mug of cold water, and the day was saved.

The same afternoon, the army came to the hospitals rescue and filled the boilers with thousands of gallons of water, so that we then had some heat. In the physiotherapy department there was a small hydro-therapy pool, so that was filled with a few thousand gallons of water, and of course could be heated by steam. This was used by patients and nurses alike for washing, and when nursing staff and other residential staff went off duty they carried a variety of containers so that they could have a wash. The army came every day with water until the main was repaired and we had running water again.

Mrs. C. A. Corles, (now living in Harborne) and her late husband Horace, moved into 519 Bristol Road South in 1970. No doubt the proximity to the adjacent house 517, on the corner of Whitehill Lane, a hostel for nursing staff, and the coming and going to the Woodlands opposite, soon resulted in their commitment to being involved in fund-raising.

Within a year of the formation of the League of Friends, Connie Corles became a member of the committee in late 1975. Connie has an immense collection of her own photographs, which bring out her voluminous memories of hospital activity, (but admits to having a bad habit of losing cameras), particularly of the Woodlands Fetes, which she was to revive and revitalise, which always took place on the second Saturday of July.

Looking at an aerial photograph of Woodlands, Connie readily recalled that virtually all available open spaces, on the fete day, would have some stand, display, exhibit or activity. "That's where the pony rides were; that's where Horace stood counting the monies as they were brought in from the stalls." etc.

The Minutes of the League of Friends show that Connie took on the role of Chairman of the Social and Fund-raising Sub-committee in September 1976. She was much involved in helping to organise the Oswestry to Birmingham Sponsored Run (referred to in Chapter 9) and instrumental in running 'a Mozart Evening'; 'a Palm Court Trio concert'; 'Flower Demonstration in the Rabone Hall' etc. In the Spring 1981, League of Friends, Newsletter, Michael Cadbury was to say:

"... Apart from the direct appeals to the public, trusts and business, which other members of the committee have undertaken, the planning of coffee mornings, lectures, musical evenings and the Fetes, have all been her work. These efforts, with raffles, flag days and like attractions, have brought in immense support for the Hospital."

This 'memory' is so important in that it shows an enthusiasm representative of the many people who have given freely of their time and effort to the needs of the R.O.H. and of course still do.

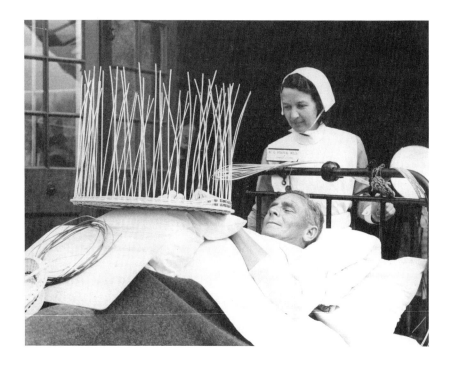

Basketry: Woodlands, April 1938
Source: R.T.C.

Chapter 9

On to 1995

Sections

- The Hydrotherapy Pool

- The League of Friends
  inclusive of
  The Research and Teaching Centre
  M.R.I.
  Fight for Survival

Hydrotherapy Pool

A report by the Physiotherapy School, on behalf of the Council for Professions Supplementary to Medicine, back in November 1967, noted the inadequacy of the 'present' Hydrotherapy Pool. The, then, House Committee recommending that a fund should be established within the Special Services Account for the eventual provision of a suitable hydrotherapy pool, to which the Regional Hospital Board agreed. Two years later consideration was being given to the specification and siting of the pool and an estimate of cost was £15,000.

Various fund raising activities were organised, including that by the Coach and Horses Charity Committee, who had agreed to act as a co-ordinating body. By the end of January 1971 the fund stood at £3,600 Students of the Physiotherapy School under its previous Head, Miss Horsfall, donated £1,000. together with valuable contributions from hospital staff and nursing staffs of both Woodlands and Forelands.

The first sketch plan was produced in May 1972, by which time the estimated cost had risen to £50,000, excluding furniture, equipment and fees. Six months later the Regional Hospital Board were looking to a viable scheme at a cost of £30,000. One year on the total estimate cost was £64,000 and by July 1973 - £86,000 followed one month later by £100,000 with an anticipated start date 'in at least five months time'. Tenders were being invited in April 1975 and in the following December saw the estimate, inclusive of building engineering fees, furniture and equipment, of £169,500.

On April the 11th 1980, a letter to Mr. Jocelyn Cadbury clarified the position re the voluntary efforts of the Coach and Horses, "... the cost was much greater than had been anticipated and eventually the scheme was taken over by the then Birmingham Regional Hospital Board, which also accepted, as a contribution to it, the money collected from the voluntary activities up to that point." (a final figure of £37,000 was handed over to the Authority, £20,000 of which coming from registered charities all over the country.)

A letter from the Administrator of the Royal Orthopaedic Hospital, on the 30th July 1981, to the Linen Service Manger announced:-

" The time is now fast approaching for the new pool to be brought into use, the remedial work is currently in hand and it is anticipated that it will be completed and the pool ready for functioning in early September. ... In the interests of getting everything prepared I would be grateful if these stocks could be issued between now and September 1st.

50 towels per day.   50 draw sheets per day.   50 top sheets per day.

50 pillow cases per day.   30 dressing gowns per day."

This being followed by a requisition for 'track suits to be supplied for the Clinical Staff involved in the Hydrotherapy Pool.'

In the foregoing information I have only given the facts re the time scale, and ever increasing costs, of the plan for the hydrotherapy pool, I leave it to the Birmingham Evening Mail, on 4th November 1981 to tell the hidden detail:-

£196,000 pool holds water at last

and

Helen's healing dip is 13 years late

by Philip Lynn

Medical Correspondent.

It took some believing when 14 year old Helen Joyner was seen to take a healing dip in the hydrotherapy pool at 'The Woodlands' Royal Orthopaedic Hospital, Northfield, Birmingham. For this was the pool that had baffled pool-makers, architects and builders since Helen was being sponged in a bath. Until today it had stubbornly refused to hold water, and for 13 years had been the despair of fund-raisers and hospital staff.

Nobody has ever discovered why the pool defied the builders efforts. It has been filled and refilled, and each time the same ominous cracks have appeared. Until this week, in readiness for tomorrow's opening, it was finally filled for Helen of Lickey Coppice, Rednal, to take her dip. Special expansion joints fitted between the tiles proved to be the answer.

So long has it taken for the 21 ft., by 14 ft., pool to hold water that the original estimated cost of £15,000 has risen to a staggering £196,000. At tomorrow's official opening, Mr. Jocelyn Cadbury, M.P. for Northfield, who has raised the matter in the House of Commons, will stand with representatives of a now almost-forgotten charity - the Coach and Horses, Castle Bromwich, pool fund. Customers of the pub promised to raise the original £15,000 but as costs rose, pulled out after the fund topped £37,000 handing the cash over to the NHS.

The League of Friends

This introduction to the League of Friends, is based upon the 'minutes for the first three years of its existence' from December 1974 to December 1977.

An inaugural meeting was held at the Woodlands on Thursday 19th December 1974, at which Mr. Michael Cadbury, the Chairman of the Steering Committee, explained the suggested constitution and aims of a League of Friends for the three Orthopaedic Hospitals, the Woodlands, Forelands and Broad Street, to an audience of about eighty members of the public, staff and retired staff. Mr. Cadbury making it clear that a League of Friends would not in any way supersede the roles of other voluntary organisations. A vote was taken on the proposal that a League of Friends be formed (after a buffet lunch) and it was carried unanimously. The Officers of the League appointed were:-

President:	Mrs. Laurence Cadbury.
Vice-Presidents:	Sir Eric Clayson.Mrs. B. Kenrick.
	Mr. Anthony Bowlby. Mr. Frank Price.
	Mr. Derek Cotton. Mr. T. Donovan.
	Sir Joseph Hunt.Mr. F. G. Allan.
	Sir Ivan Stedeford.
Chairman;	Mr. Michael Cadbury.
Secretary;	Rev. D. Collyer.
Assistant Secretary:	Mrs. F. Williamson.
Treasurer:	Mr. J. Black.
Committee Members:	Mrs. Williams: vacancies on committee to be filled later.

I have referred earlier to the founding of a League of Friends at the Robert Jones/Agnes Hunt Orthopaedic Hospital, Oswestry back in 1949, and now with reference to the 1975 Journal of that Hospital, issue No.15, there are two items worthy of mention.

On the State of Public Health. The following disorders are listed among the causes of death for the year 1719 in the City of London:-

Pain in ye head	1.	Swelling in ye knee	1.
Lethargy	7.	Twisting of ye Guts	54.
Rising of ye Lights	76.	Suddenly	118.

On a sober note however, and in the same issue, the death is announced of Mr. F. G. Allan. (*one of the new Vice-Presidents of the newly formed League of Friends) Francis Glen Allan, a pioneer of orthopaedic surgery, died on the 15th January 1975 at the age of seventy-four. He started his orthopaedic career in 1923 as a house-surgeon to Rowley Bristow at St. Thomas's Hospital, London, and in 1928 became assistant to Mr. Naughton Dunn in Birmingham and at the Shropshire Orthopaedic Hospital, Oswestry, later to become the Robert Jones and Agnes Hunt Orthopaedic Hospital.

Allan's main work was at the Royal Orthopaedic Hospital, Birmingham, and at the Children's Hospital and at the Warwickshire Royal Orthopaedic Hospital, Coleshill. When Dunn died in 1939, Allan became assistant to A. O. Parker at Oswestry and, in due course, succeeded him as Senior Consultant Surgeon and Chief of the Hereford team of Surgeons, maintaining the position up to his retirement in 1966. .He continued to work for the Hospital's Management Committee up to the time of his death.

Francis Allan was a man of quiet charm, ready humour and evident shyness. His quiet reserved nature completely hid a quite extraordinary surgical courage, inventiveness and determination, which lead him to tackle orthopaedic problems from which the majority of his contemporaries, and many of today's (1975) surgeons, would shrink. Allan was a Master Surgeon whose clinical experience was rivalled by few.

* note. Sir Ivan A. R. Stedeford also passed away before the first full meeting of the League of Friends, in January 1975.

The League of Friends Committee were soon considering Administrative arrangements with a proposal that patients should be kept fully informed of activities, possibly by the use of printed cards and leaflets, with a collecting box at the entrance to all wards, communication being very important and that a quarterly newsletter would be an ideal vehicle. A priority of projects soon found the announcement that work was to start shortly on an adventure playground for the children's ward, the cost being around £700, the money having been donated by the Variety Club of Great Britain and the playing Fields Association. It would be the first playground of its kind for handicapped children.

In March 1975 a further priority list was produced by Miss Reed, Matron, and Mr. M.H.M.Harrison, which included:- An Image Intensifier enabling surgeons to operate and look at x-rays, cost £6,000 to £9,000, - Air Driven power tool, - X-ray viewing screen in a demonstration cabinet, - Tape and slide equipment, - a Bowling Green for patients, - a Lifting Hoist for each ward, - an Admission Unit for all people who are received at the hospital, - improvements in the nurses home, - Showers on all wards, - Non-slip trays for patients meals, - Cantilever tables. Discussions followed to consider whether to aim for several small things to start with or launch the appeal for a major project . It was decided that the target should be high, and "Because of their interests and experience a working party consisting of Rev. David Collyer, Mr. Hand, Mr. Black and the hospital staff was formed to give more accurate specific information and detailed costs."

The League of Friends became a Registered Charity by April 1975, and at that time Max Harrison was addressing the question of collecting boxes, looking into the experiences of other hospitals. A box in the wall seemed to be the only practical solution. Subsequently the League of Friends were to purchase two small wall safes at thirty pounds each, one for the Broad Street Outpatient Department and the other at Woodlands. The working party soon agreed to aiming for a high target over a long period, the committee accepting that £75,000 should be the aim over a period of seven years. A sub-committee was formed including Mr. Hand, Mr. Parnham and Rev. David Collyer to consider the ways and means of launching a 1975 appeal.

A first newsletter was being mooted in June, Mr. Pitt reporting that he had enough subject matter for the first copy. Miss Reed and Mr. Parnham formed a sub-committee to assist. Mr. Cadbury was to produce an inaugural letter, news items about the Woodlands by Mr. Rickett, and the administrative staff were arranging to print a staff newsletter. By September production was well in hand, the 'newsletter had been drafted and will be printed shortly.' The Hospital Authorities' were to meet half the cost of production, 250 copies costing £175. The hospital staff will provide the paper and cut the stencil and volunteers will be asked to help with duplicating and collating.

In October 1975 Mr. Jack Payne was invited to become a Vice-President, and it was suggested that a trolley service be started for patients in the Woodlands, arranging for ladies from the Friends to take the trolley around, it being stocked from the W.R.V.S. shop. By the following December, the Trolley had arrived and was in the Chaplain's office (!). The Rev. David Collyer had also officially opened the Adventure Playground.

In January 1976 Mr. Cadbury and Mr. Parnham had written officially to the hospital asking for the latest position concerning the Hydrotherapy pool. At that time the cost stood at £178,000 with the pool fund being £37,000. Miss Reed, in May spoke of the need at Forelands of a 'Mini Co-Ro Bed.' A special rocking bed for paralysed patients, which, with accessories, would cost about £800. With the Readers Digest having published a list of charities to whom they contribute from unclaimed prizes it was decided to ask for their help, as special projects, for either Four Co-Ro Beds at £800 each or £12,000 to re-equip a ward.

Miss Reed later wrote a letter of appreciation to the League of Friends following the gift of this bed, "... It is a marvellous piece of equipment, which has saved the nurses many hours of 'backbreaking' lifting already. We had a suitable patient ready to put in the bed when it arrived at the end of June. She was a lady we had received from the Midland Spinal Injuries Unit at Oswestry. ... the healing process has been so rapid that we have to monitor it more frequently ... Needless to say we are all delighted with the results, also the patient's general health and moral has greatly improved."

The October Newsletter states some of the things that have been achieved during the first year. The Children's playground outside Ward 11; 25 new types of Locker/Wardrobe in the 'Authority' renovated and rewired Ward 8; A donation was given to the team of Consultants, Registrars and Student Doctors in training, for special equipment; A donation for the Nurses' Home for facilities in washing and drying clothes; The Trolley service, operated by Miss Elsie Grayland.

Plans were going ahead for a sponsored run from Oswestry to Birmingham on 23rd April 1977 . Miss Reed, with a typically caring gesture, suggested that the runners should be seen off at Oswestry as well as being greeted at Woodlands. This 'run' at first sight reads as being just another fund-raising event, however as the June Newsletter tells, it was indeed a story of determination and courage exhibited by the three men taking part in the run. One of the group Mr. M. E. Murray of Northfield wrote, " As a child I spent several years in the Woodlands after contracting polio of the leg, my wife has had an operation on her back, so we are both thankful to the hospital staff. To show my appreciation I aim to organise and participate in a sponsored run ... the money raised to be used for urgent needs."

The team of men, Malcolm Murray (age 31), John Bayliss (age 31), Alan Rogers (age 27) with two accompanying drivers, Trevor Southall and Roger Martin, stayed overnight at their own expense at Oswestry, and at 7.15 am. they set off. Each one doing three mile legs, enabled them to face the elements, a bright sunny morning but very strong winds, later turning to rain. At the end of the 27 miles (each runner) they were met at 6 pm. at the hospital gates by patients out on trolley chairs, together with the Chief Administrative Officer, the Matron, Miss Reed, and members of the League of Friends Committee, together with of course their own families. Drinks and a meal were provided by the Hospital Authority. They were to donate the splendid sum of £365.95 to be used particularly for the children's Ward.

An update of gifts from the League of Friends up to the end of 1977 shows:-

20 Cantilever Type Overbed Tables;   1. Static Bicycle.

A Two Pedestal Desk.   4. Elbow Chairs in the Outpatient Department.

2. Automatic Washing Machines. 2. Tumbler Dryers.

2. Electric Steam Irons.   1. Ironing Table.

2. Telescopic Clothes Dryers - for the Nursing Staff

Cine-equipment, Slide Projector and slide tray for Students and Medical Staff.

1. Bath, Shower and Therapy Unit with leg support.

Toilet Chair and Safety Black Belt.

14. Extra Arden -Type Wardrobe Lockers.

4. Portable Television Sets and various games for the Children's Ward

15 Chairs and 16 Lockers.

To this date we have seen the considerable contribution to the daily needs of the patients and staff of the hospital, by the League of Friends. Clearly the future holds, as the Friends influence is consolidated, opportunities for large Capital Projects, and they certainly intend pressing ahead. The R.T.C.; the M.R.I. being but two such projects. One 'event' of which they were not yet aware was to demand the complete commitment of the entire hospital Staff and the determination of the League of Friends to ensure that the Woodlands would successfully ride another storm.

A most informative booklet produced by Mr. M. B. Rickett, on behalf of the League of Friends, dated June 1981 marked an Appeal for a Research and Teaching Centre, entitled Royal Orthopaedic Hospital, Birmingham - Profile - South Birmingham Health Authority. With the Proposal:-

"The envisaged centre is one which will allow those undertaking special clinical development and research to meet, discuss and store data. It would comprise in the main a Conference Room, a Research Unit, a Research Records Office and an Assessment Centre. Not only would those working in the hospital be involved here but it will provide a place for research workers attached to different projects. It is also hoped that it will give a stimulus to research between the orthopaedic discipline and those of rheumatology, bone metabolism and geriatrics. The cost of the building and equipment at current prices is £500,000.

The Booklet outlines the required Building and Research Facilities, and a proposed plan. Sources of Support, a Short History, and the existing state of play, intended to support the need for a teaching centre, "The nature of orthopaedics has changed dramatically since the war, although we no longer have to treat the severe deformities of tuberculosis and poliomyelitis. The workload has however increased because of the dramatic arrival of new surgical techniques... The hospital has kept pace with this and last year admitted the most orthopaedic patients to any one hospital in the whole of the West Midlands... More than one third come from outside the Birmingham area."

The Article continues with information on the Birmingham Orthopaedic Training Programme, which had been established in 1971, which played a very important part in the education of surgeons,. Also being the centre of undergraduates in the teaching of orthopaedics to Birmingham University, and with the Nursing School and the Physiotherapy School it provides the centre of reference for all those training in the management and rehabilitation of the crippling diseases.

The School of Orthopaedic Nursing details, include the programme of training:- Orthopaedic Nurse Training may be achieved by following one of two routes. Young people aged 17 years with a minimum of five GCE 'O' levels (or CSE equivalent) may commence in September a twenty month course leading to the Orthopaedic Nursing Certificate. This must be followed by general training at a hospital of the student's choice. Trained nurses may undertake a twelve month post-basic course which commences in January, March and July. State Registered Nurses on successful completion of the course are awarded the ONC, and State Enrolled Nurses are awarded the Diploma in Orthopaedic Nursing. Experience is gained at all three sites of the hospital and at the Birmingham Accident Hospital.

The Hospital Activity at the year 1979 was:-

Inpatient		Outpatients	
Average daily number of beds	239	New Outpatients	5,027
Admissions	3,185	Total Attendances	28,355
Day Cases	706	New Physiotherapy	4,767
New Physiotherapy	1731	Total Attendances	60,660
New Occupational Therapy	614	New Chiropody	39
Total Operations	2,400	Total Attendances	130
		New Surgical Appliances	561
		Total Attendances	5,349

	Inpatients	New Outpatients
Scoliosis	194	170
Perthes Disease	51	25
Bone Tumour	94	
Total Hip Replacement	399	

The Full Complement of Hospital Staffing being:-

Senior Members of Staff

Mr.M. B. Rickett, AHA., Administrator. Mr. S. Crews, Deputy Administrator.

Miss F. Poulter, Assistant Administrator, (Outpatient Department).

Consultant Orthopaedic Surgeons

Mr. M. H. M. Harrison, M.Ch.Orth., FRCS. Mr. C. P. Cotterill, FRCSE.

Mr. H. Piggott, FRCS.   Mr. R. Sneath, FRCS.

Mr. J. R. Pearson, FRCS.   Mr.P. J. Mulligan, FRCSG., FRCS

Mr. J. James, FRCS.   Director of Studies.

Mr. A. G. Thompson, FRCS.   Mr. R. S. N. Duke, FRCS.

Mr. K. N. Norcross, FRCS.   Mr. J. O'Garra, FRCS.

Mr. T. D. J. Botting, FRCS.   Mr. O. N. Tubbs, FRCS.

Mr. J. J.McMillan, MB.ChB .FRCS.Ed.   Dr. A. J. Popert, FRCS.

Consultant Radiologist

Dr. P. Jacobs, MB., ChB., FRCP., MRCS., LRCP., FRCR., FFR., DMRD.

Consultant Anaesthetists

Dr. P. Dennison.   Dr. J. Prosser.   Dr. J. Davies.   Dr. G. Hall Davies.

Dr. R. Johnson.   Dr. V. Bates.   Dr. R. Lewthwaite.

Dr. U. Smith.   Dr. A. M. H. Nicholls.

Honorary Consultant

Professor J. T. Scales, FRCS., Consultant in Bio-Medical Engineering.

Professor Burwell, University of Birmingham.   Mr. W. Scrase.

Research Assistants   Dr. Hall.   Dr. Turner.   Mr. Gardecki.

Staff Medical Officer   Dental Surgeons   Senior Nursing Officer

Dr. Buchanan   Mr. Baker   Miss P. M. Reed, SRN.,

Mr. Jennings.   SCM., ONC.

Nursing Officers

Miss J. Shaw, SRN., ONC.   Miss C. Newell, SRN., ONC.

Miss M. Selman, SRN., ONC.   Mrs. C. Boswell Munday, SRN., ONC.

Mrs. P. Kesterton, SRN., ONC., Forelands.

Nursing School Mr. L. Evans, Senior Tutor.

Physiotherapy School

Miss E. Jahn, MCSP., Dip. TP.- Principal.

Miss S. Kelly, MCSP., Dip. TP.- Deputy.   Miss K. Conran, MCSP., Dip. TP.

Miss N. Burl, MCSP., Dip. TP.   Mr. K. Stopani, MCSP., Dip. TP.

Sister Andrena, MCSP.

Mrs.P.Cockersole,MCSP.,Dip. TP.

Superintendent Radiographer   Miss P. Mitchell, DCR., SRR.

Superintendent Physiotherapist   Mrs. R. Madeley, MCSP., SRP.

Senior Occupational Therapist   Mrs. D. Penrose.

Staff Pharmacist   Miss C.Hassall, B.Pharm.Hons., MSc., MPS.

Orthopaedic Appliance Workshop   Mr. D. Minnis, Head of Department.

Clinic Superintendent   Miss Jones, ONC., MCSP.

Special Clinics

Scoliosis	Rheumatoid	Tumour
Mr. H. Piggott	Mr. J. Pearson	Mr. R. Sneath
Perthes	Club Foot	Spinal
Mr. M. H. M. Harrison	Mr. C. P. Cotterill	Mr. A. G. Thompson
Hand Surgery	Arthroscopy	
Mr. P. J. Mulligan	Mr. O. N. Tubbs	

Minutes of the Research and Teaching Centre show that Mr. P. J. Mulligan in a letter dated 12th. April 1979, sent to the Dean of the Faculty of Medicine, University of Birmingham, outlined the reasoning for the erection of a building for Teaching and Research "... The Hospital provides a complete orthopaedic service and in recent years has developed specialist interests. The management of spinal deformities in children, bone tumour surgery, major spinal reconstruction, special children's clinics and hand surgery ... There is a strong tradition within the Hospital of providing highly knowledgable nurses, physiotherapists and orthotists. ... it is a training school for each of these disciplines ... With this background it seems obvious that the Royal Orthopaedic Hospital should improve its position as a centre for orthopaedic training in Birmingham. With this in mind the medical staff and administrators are now developing plans to establish an Institute for the management of locomotor disease within the Hospital and is a step nearer towards establishing a full department of locomotor system surgery within Birmingham and in the university of Birmingham. The first phase ... is to erect a building for teaching and research ... The data of major projects already in progress can then be gathered into one place. The X-ray collection of Dr. P. Josephs, our currently outstanding radiologist, would also be given a position of prominence."

"... The funding of such a building would be met out of monies to be collected by the League of Friends of the Royal Orthopaedic Hospital, whose Chairman is Mr. Michael Cadbury ..."

The Sector Administrator, in a letter dated 6th November 1980, to the District Administrator noted that the Committee of the League of Friends had advised the Hospital Management Team that they would like to launch an appeal, looking to seriously pursue in collaboration with them the proposed development, subject to the support of the DMT and AHA.

A meeting was held on 12th January 1981, to discuss the initial stages in the organisation of the League of Friends appeal to fund a Research and Teaching Block, between Mr. Mulligan, Rev. David Collyer and Mr. B. M. Rickett. The suggested site was to be opposite the existing conference room on an area currently occupied by several gardeners' huts and a greenhouse. On the 13th June 1981, Mr. Mulligan wrote to the Marquis of Hertford, referring back to "the honour of your family's intervention when the hospital was privileged to be designated with the Royal Charter, in 1888," inviting his patronage for the Appeal. The following October, in gratefully acknowledging the Marquis of Hertford's acceptance, Mr. Mulligan again wrote, sending the Marquis a draft letter for use in an appeal brochure, and asking for a facsimile signature, also for his signature on about twenty of the letters for the Special Appeal.

The Appeal was officially launched on Thursday 25th February 1982, with the media being invited to a Press Conference in the School of Nursing at the Woodlands Hospital. Within two months of the launch the Rev. David Collyer writes to Mr. Mulligan:

"I felt it appropriate to write to you after a few weeks of our programme of circulating patients passing through the hospital's hands. There is no doubt that this programme is an unqualified success. Very substantial donations arrive daily, frequently occupied by letters of gratitude. I would think that to date we are averaging about £25 per letter, although the contributions have ranged from £2 to £500.Having spent many years in the appeals business, with its regular slog of sending and signing letters, I felt that those who are actually engaged in this enterprise should be notified of their success. The appeal is moving towards £40,000, which is the most successful launch that I have ever known." At the Appeals Committee meeting of 22nd September 1982, the fund is stated to be approaching £100,000. and by 27th February 1984 the fund stood at £185,342.81p, the money being raised from; grateful patients, hospital staff organising a variety of fund raising activities including Bring and Buys, pantomime concerts, shows, sponsored events etc. The annual hospital fete had raised over £3,000.

Miss Felicity Kendal appeared on BBC Television on 20th February 1984 to appeal on our behalf and this alone raised £72,116.73. The Birmingham Post of May 1st 1984 under the heading 'Felicitous Act', and the Birmingham Evening Mail May 4th 1984, 'Hospital praise for fantastic Felicity, both acknowledged her effort in boosting the Appeal Fund to some £300,000, as a result of the Television Appeal which also brought in an additional donation of £75,000 from an American Company. Felicity Kendal came to Birmingham, firstly to visit the Orthopaedic Hospital and secondly to appear on 'Pebble Mill at One' to receive the cheque from that American Company.

The Stone Laying Ceremony took place on 4th December 1985, unveiled, of course, by Felicity Kendal. The formal hand-over was arranged for 2nd June 1986. Good news for the hospital gardeners came but two days later when Mr. Mee, District Building Officer explained that he was going to tender for turfing and seeding of the external grounds, and was seeking the advice of the W.M.R.H.A. Landscaping Experts. The Research and Teaching Centre was formally opened on Thursday 10th December 1987, by Sir James Ackers.

The decision to close the Forelands was reported in a local newspaper dated 7th August 1986, (this is not taken from the League of Friends Newsletters) under the headline 'Hospital Fight is Defeated'.

The closing order had come despite a 6,000 signature petition, public meetings and protests. A stay of execution of 18 months had been achieved, with the building not being shut until a new ward had been built, probably at Woodlands, and with the hope that the team work achieved at Forelands could continue elsewhere.

The remaining part of this history is based on information gleaned from the League of Friends Quarterly Newsletters 1989 to 1995. Produced, by that period in Booklet Form. On the inside cover, and repeated throughout this period, an insight into their activities is given. 'The target for each year is in the region of ten thousand pounds.' 'Amongst items recently purchased have been chairs for waiting areas in the Outpatients Department at Broad Street, curtains for various wards, colour television sets, a catering display cabinet for the staff canteen, and new stimulators to reduce pain. Anatomical models of the human brain and leg were provided for the newly refurbished School of Nursing. The Friends have completely furnished seven bedrooms for the patients' relatives and have donated £5,000 towards a sophisticated instrument used in knee joint surgery.

Referring to its role in the acquisition of the Research and Teaching Centre, the introduction ends 'The League of Friends continues to support the needs of patients, nursing and surgical staff. Will you help us to help them?'

In the April 1989 newsletter the death is announced of Mrs. Joyce Cadbury, O.B.E. who had held the Presidency of the League of Friends since its inauguration in 1974.

The Articles throughout these newsletters, from every corner of hospital life are most interesting and newsworthy. The Radiographer and the Patient being one written with tongue in cheek " If you've worked in an X-ray department for a few years it's very easy to forget that an x-ray room

Helen's healing dip
copyright: Birmingham Post & Mail

'The good life for a trainee brickie'

Birmingham born actress Felicity Kendal samples the Good Life with bricklayers Andrew Howes (left) and Damien Ivory, as they lay the foundation stones for the new Research and Teaching Centre.

copyright: Birmingham Post & Mail

full of equipment can look a bit intimidating to patients and even quite frightening for small children. It's a joke amongst student radiographers that you get an extra mark in your technique exam every time you write down 'reassure the patient' (in fact if you wrote it a hundred times, you'd be sure to pass!)."

The League of Friends tells 'Where the Money Goes'. £6,790 having been spent in the last few months on - a Pulse Therapy Machine - Stained Glass Windows for the Chapel - Knee Exerciser - Pegasus Air-Wave Bed - 5 Nerve Stimulators - Fitting Room Carpet, Broad Street - Optokopy Control System - 3 Resuscitation Trolleys - Multi-Grill, for the Catering Department.

The Autumn 1989 newsletter brings to the fore the first mention (in material available to the author of this history) made to 'Building a Healthy Birmingham.' Introduced by Mr. Peter Jubb, the then Secretary of the League of Friends, he says; "... As Friends of the Woodlands might expect the main topic for discussion and action has over the past few months been that of the effect on the Woodlands of the proposed hospitals reorganisation. Whilst precise details are complicated, the essence would be for the orthopaedic and related services to be based on District General Hospitals with the South Birmingham share of these going to the Queen Elizabeth and Selly Oak Hospitals".

The League of Friends committee has expressed its views to the Chairman of the West Midlands Regional Health Authority, and the staff of the Woodlands formed its own action committee to defend the Royal Orthopaedic Hospital. (Once again I feel that we have been here before, some 40 and 20 years before).

And who gets the 'ball-rolling'? .*It was Andy Hill, the Chef at Woodlands, who was fast off the mark with a petition to 'Save the Royal Orthopaedic Hospital's services, following the publication of the. WMRHA, plan, resulting in the raising of a 26,000 signature petition. This petition becoming also the Action Committee's petition'. * So says Mr. John Churchman, X-ray Department, Chairman of that Action Committee.

John continues: "We were greatly helped by patients, families, staff and members of the public who took the petition to their own communities, places of work, churches etc. Support came from far and wide on one day from Leamington, Liverpool and Bolton. A mother brought 1,000 signatures from Northern Ireland after her daughter had been to the Woodlands for treatment. (We have, of course, been campaigning for the retention and development of all Royal Orthopaedic services, including the very specialised skills found at Broad Street)".

"We decided to have a day out ... setting up a stall at the Shopping Centre in Northfield (the staff could not have been more helpful). Mr. John Sims did an amazing job attracting customers for hours on end.(sustained by two packets of lozenges!). Six Thousand signatures were collected between nine and five o'clock. Another morning on the streets of Northfield, with a great rush of petitions reached that 26,000, a figure too big for the RHA. to disregard easily. The people who ran the days, and helped to man the stalls, or lay in wait in the car park, were nurses, porters, physiotherapists, radiographers, a chef, friends of the hospital, former patients and their families."

"We arranged to hand in the petition at the same time as the Save Our Hospitals Action Group delivered theirs, to Sir James Ackers at the RHA. headquarters. Radio and Television came along to record the event. The strength of concern about the proposals was made very clear"

Press releases of 23rd October referred to evident changes to the original proposals. "Our plan to replace services now being provided in the old deteriorating specialty hospitals into brand new facilities on the appropriate Medical Centre ...". "... The Medical Centre (i.e. Q.E./Selly Oak) will constitute the District General Hospital for South Birmingham, and the Selly Oak component will be expanded to include ... the Orthopaedic Hospital including bone tumour services, a major rehabilitation centre ...". "... South Birmingham Medical Centre will be developed to provide at Selly Oak ... new facilities for ...orthopaedic rehabilitation.".

The inferences to be drawn were:- Selly Oak will become the centre for Orthopaedic medicine which would presumably be maintained there as an integrated whole. (this was a welcome revision). However the present Royal Orthopaedic Hospital sites, Woodlands and Broad Street, would presumably be phased out.

The Future of the Woodlands is the headline for the Spring 1990 Newsletter update. The R.H.A. has conceded the need for various services of the hospital to be kept together, so that the bone tumour services will stay with the other orthopaedic services. On the other hand there still seems to be a large cut in orthopaedic bed numbers ... amounting to some 80 beds when those presently at Selly Oak and the General Hospital are included. Under the plan a new orthopaedic unit will be built at Selly Oak (where the number of beds will rise to 1,000). When this opens in the year 2,000 Woodlands and Broad Street will close. (In fact the R.H.A. manager has said that Broad Street may well close earlier, with the bulk of its services being moved either to Selly Oak or, on a temporary basis to Woodlands).

The R.H.A. says, in favour of a move to Selly Oak, "... patients will have better access to intensive care facilities and to physicians from other medical specialities ... they will be part of a major trauma and orthopaedic centre and a major teaching hospital. ... reprovision at Selly Oak will include the Research and Education Centre (R.T.C.!) and the transfer of donated equipment."

The Woodlands is determined to keep the pressure on. "Whatever happens in the long term we are right to be concerned now about aspects of the plan. Building at Selly Oak will not start for another eight years. Will the money really be there then? The R.H.A. forecasts a need for a real annual increase in revenue spending over 12 years or more of the whole plan. If this is not forthcoming will the plans be delayed again and again or cancelled after 8 years had elapsed, during which time Woodlands and Broad Street had been allowed to deteriorate irretrievably."

Life must proceed however, Physiotherapy for Specials are referred to in Summer 1990. Specials being patients at this hospital under the care of Mr. Sneath who require a special type of bone replacement, being referred from all over the country, as the Woodlands and the Royal National Orthopaedic Hospital, Middlesex, are the only two hospitals in this country that do this operation.

Now for the Woodlands Scanner Appeal, for £2,000,000. a large amount of money to raise but the benefit to patients is enormous. The Rev. David

Collyer explains that the first £1 million will be spent on a M.R.I. (Magnetic Resonance Imager) Scanner which has been underwritten by our interest-free loan, so that we can make an early start on the programme. The Day Ward opened, at Woodlands, in 1988 had been a successful project. The League of Friends having kindly agreed to fund upgrading the Ward at the cost of almost £20,000.

A charming article appears in the Autumn issue from Mr. Jack Payne, who had taken the post of President of the League of Friends, following the death of Mrs. Joyce Cadbury. He tells of his association with the Woodlands going back to 1930, when still at school. The father of one of his friends organised some 20 or 30 car owners into taking 'cripples for a run in the country'. "... Later I had a car of my own and was able to do my bit ... my wife later joined in with her car and, moreover, became a hospital visitor. ... Moreover I have been a patient myself, with two new hip joints". (at that time Jack was approaching his 80th birthday). Any one knowing Jack Payne will smile at his next comment, this mild and most friendly man, with a twinkle in his eye.

"Two of the most precious memories I have of the Hospital are, recovering consciousness after one operation to find the Matron holding my hand and whispering sweet nothings. The other was a visit from the Chaplain, the Rev. David Collyer who, with his Deaconess, asked me if I would like to take Holy Communion. I was very impressed and will always be grateful to David for his kind action. Who knows, this may have been the first step towards the Anglican Church for a life-long Non-Conformist.". (There can be few Birmingham people who would not know of Mr. Payne, in that there can hardly have been a Birmingham, or even West Midland' suburb that did not have at least one Payne's Shoe repair shop, during the years 1908 to the mid 1970's.)

Are you being served? Well certainly the ladies group running the Trolley service, who help Mrs. May Calder to take the service to all of the Hospital Wards every Tuesday and Thursday are eagerly awaited, laden with 'goodies' from the WRVS shop. The trolley when fully laden is quite heavy especially over parts of the hilly terrain which exists at Woodlands. The cheerful offers from patients of "... we would like to help you push but ..." is

Directions to caring. 1997
photo: Brian Jones

a regular call. The static shop run by the WRVS. stocks an ever increasing range and they make a lovely cup of coffee or tea and delicious hot buttered toast.

We have heard of the squirrels gnawing at the Physiotherapy School roof. That forgotten, the visitors who always have memories of the wildlife in the hospital grounds watching the squirrels play, can now 'buy' one. "We have now made our very own 'Squirrel Pin' which is suitable to be attached to a tie or jacket. They are currently being sold in aid of the * Centenary Appeal to raise money for the M.R.I.Scanner."

*this being the Granting of Royal Status to the R.O.H. in 1888.

The Woodlands Travel Club organised and run by John and Sandra Sims since its formation, then as part of the League of Friends, in 1985, announces that the 'day trips and holidays, to date, had raised over £7,000, of which £3,000 had been donated to the M.R.I. Scanner Appeal.' At Summer 1991 the appeal had reached £40,000, half the cost of the Scanner itself, leaving a further £1 million for building and other costs. A raffle for David Platt's England Shirt raised £2,707.

Mrs. May Calder retired after many years of tireless work from the Trolley service. Dr. P.B.Pynsent, Ph.D. Director of Research wrote that the official ceremony of laying the foundation stone of the Scanner Building took place on Wednesday 17th July 1991, performed by Mr. Frank Graves, OBE. Chairman of the new South Birmingham Health Authority. The current balance of the Appeal Fund had reached £453,568. Nine months later the 'Scanner had arrived at the Woodlands and is operational' and by Autumn 1992 'This marvellous machine is now in full use for the screening of patients. Morning sessions are being used by South Birmingham Health Authority. Afternoon sessions which have been purchased by neighbouring Health Authorities are being used for their patients.' There is no better way, to show early success than to receive the appreciation of a patient.

"I was fortunate to have an M.R.I. Scan shortly after the Centre opened. The images produced precise detailed diagnosis enabling successful surgery being undertaken. My excruciating pain has gone and I am eternally grateful." The Squirrel badges are selling well, for by the end of 1992, 37,000 had been purchased resulting in the raising of £24,000 for the

Scanner Appeal.

Mid 1993 and the outlook for the possible re-siting of the Woodlands is still bleak. "...Transfer of the main R.O.H. activities on a fairly short time scale to the General Hospital ... Nevertheless some functions (Research and Teaching Centre, M.R.I. Scanner etc.) will continue on site and the time table for change may yet again be adjusted." At a cost of some £12,000 the hospital had acquired an Arthroscope, for the inspection of joints.

Mrs. Cathy Matthews, Director of Nursing, who had succeeded Mrs Stella Noon in 1991 (see the 'Three Matrons' Profile, Chapter 10), states the hospital work-loads as at December 1992. "... Activity had increased by over 100%, allowing us to meet our contracted work-load. By the end of January 1993 we will have completed that work-load ... additional loading to come being G.P. Fundholders, E.C.R's and Private work. ... All staff within the hospital have worked tremendously hard ... to regain its credibility and be seen as a viable place to send patients ... the patient care was maintained and all the staff saw it as a way to maintain stability of the hospital whatever its future." By the end of 1993 Cathy's matron's role has again been re-designated, to Business Manager/ Director of Nursing. The Newsletter Editor referred to "...a brief news item that the major plan 'Building a Healthy Birmingham' had been cancelled. We wait to hear what this will mean to the Royal Orthopaedic Hospital".

Meanwhile Sister H. Philpot writes in the Autumn 1993 Newsletter re the High Dependency Unit. " ... When the Unit opened it was known as the Recovery Area and the number of patients was very small. With the demands on the service and the high levels of dependency and care required by patients, its name was changed to the H.D.U. in 1993. Its role, as a thirteen bedded unit provides a service to four orthopaedic theatres, one plaster theatre and a pain clinic. ... concerned predominantly with the management of the immediate post-operative patient recovering from major surgery, and providing care for ill patients from the general wards ... HDU, has a higher nurse/patient level and support than is available on the wards ... this makes possible the early detection and treatment of problems."

The League of Friends took over, on August 14th 1993, where the WRVS.

left off, the responsibility for providing refreshments for visitors. Mrs. Wendy Cochrane and her group of helpers invited everyone coming to the Woodlands to call in for a 'cuppa'.

The Woodlands Travel Club gets further mention in the Spring Newsletter with an article that briefly outlines its early functions and development. Its modest beginning being with occasional day trips but soon expanding to wide ranging weekend events and longer holidays. Until 1994 it had operated as part of and under the charity reference of the League of Friends. With the Travel Club raising funds for many charities, travellers being invited to nominate their own charity, it soon became evident that there was a strong case for it to be hived off as a separate entity. It to be known as the Woodlands Travel Club Ltd, in effect an independent company. The Honorary Secretary of the League of Friends, at that time, Mr. Peter Jubb, makes a most fitting remark, as true today (1997), as then. "Where could one find a parallel for the 'Sims' input of time, energy and initiative for a charity".

It is also fitting to state, that John Sims, so ably supported by Sandra, is but one of the many people who have thrown their full support to the running of the voluntary aspects of the hospital, because of a personal contact. John's brother Stan having been in the hospital in 1984, under the care of Mr. Rodney Sneath.

It was November 1993 at the meeting of the League of Friends committee that the Chairman, Michael Cadbury, stated that by a decision made at Ministerial level, the Royal Orthopedic Hospital was to close on 30th March 1994, and there would be no more League of Friends meetings. John Sims was in the right position to charter a coach to carry a group and visit Tory MP's at the House of Commons to try and persuade them to request the Secretary of State to reconsider the closure. 'If and when that exercise has been completed, the committee of the League of Friends can then with confidence tell the membership that the Committee of the Royal Orthopaedic Hospital had done everything possible to keep the R.O.H. upon the Woodlands site.'

At the suggestion of Cathy Matthews, John was invited to meet the Chairman of the Medical Staff Committee, Mr. Derek McMinn, at which

John proposed setting up a meeting with the Secretary of State and Birmingham MP's at the House of Commons, and to consider a strategy to fight the closure plan. At that same meeting Mr. Andrew Thomas also a Consultant Orthopaedic Surgeon at the ROH, threw in his complete support. Mr. McMinn, Mr. Thomas together with John and Sandra Sims were to act as co-ordinators for the League of Friends

'With only 131 days to save the Hospital' it was essential that the public be notified, also that ammunition was required showing the true financial statement of the hospitals viability, and a plan for the rebuild of the Royal Orthopaedic Hospital on the Woodlands site. On the former, the ROH was treating more patients than ever before in its history and were producing a financial surplus of £700,000 pa. A blue-print for our future hospital and site was also provided.

Mr. McMinn was invited to speak on BBC Local Radio by Mr. Ed Doolan the, then, presenter of a lunch time consumer, programme at Pebble Mill. Having a listening audience of some 500,000, the support resulting was not so surprising Listeners phoning in their support. The Birmingham Evening Mail and the Birmingham Post devoted many column inches, at times whole pages, in support of the campaign, and BBC Midlands Today and the Independent Central News raised the issue through their Television news programmes. 'The Band Wagon had started to Roll'.

During the month of December 1995, 700 members of the League of Friends were writing letters, so to were all the passengers who travelled with the Woodlands Travel Club. Letters to their MP's (no matter what political persuasion) and Government Ministers, and to the Birmingham Evening Mail. Petition forms were included for them to get signed by their friends and anyone else. The Reader's Letters' in the Evening Mail every night were exhilarating. Such was the concern at the amount of letters being received from their readers, that the *Editor of the Evening Mail, Mr. Ian Dowell and the Birmingham City Council jointly sponsored what was called 'The Great Debate', which was to take place in the Birmingham Town Hall on January 22nd, 1994.

*Once again the Birmingham Mail gives its full support to the needs of the Royal Orthopaedic Hospital. 75 years before it was the Editor

Mr. H. F. Harvey.

The Parliamentary Lobby took place on 13th January 1994, at which 15 Members of Parliament were lobbied. On arrival Six MP's five Labour and one Liberal Democrat met the Coach questioning Mr. McMinn and the Consultants. Derek McMinn, Andrew Thomas, Cathy Matthews (Matron), Stella Noon (Matron retired), John Sims and, the late, Eric Millington met with Sir Norman Fowler and later Andrew Hargreaves (then Member of Parliament for Hall Green Birmingham), at which it was soon realised that there had been a comprehensive 'mail-bag' calling for non-closure. On the day of the visit Mr. McMinn was interviewed on BBC Radio 4 early morning news programmes, these, of course, being listened to by the majority of MP's. 'We were expected.'

In the afternoon a further meeting was held with Dame Jill Knight (Rodney Sneath joining the party).

The Great Debate was an astounding success, Derek McMinn speaking with great distinction and force. Many other speeches were made on behalf of several other hospitals facing the same demise. It was brought to a close by the Chairman of the W.M.R.H.A. whose final words were "the Royal Orthopaedic Hospital will be given until 1st April 1995 to remain in Balance then it will be considered for Trust Status". As John Sims said "I do not think anyone who attended the meeting fully understood the meaning of that statement. Had the closure been dropped? Had we won a stay of execution? ... All that we knew was that the hospital would not be closing on the 31st March 1994."

Trust Status was granted 1st April 1995, the Evening Mail carried photographs and news of the 'great event in the history of our hospital'.

What has to be said is that throughout the campaign to save the Woodlands, the resulting success was due to the combined efforts of every member of the Royal Orthopaedic Hospital staff, Administrators, Surgeons, Nurses, Domestics, Services, etc., (many of whom were prepared to stand up and be counted). All along the way they received magnificent support from the public, the media, radio, television and newspapers.

And of course

'the League of Friends Committee would be meeting again'.

This history now moves on to the 'Royal Orthopaedic Hospital NHS, Trust' and the dawn of the 'New Era'. However before doing so I wish to give three profiles, looking at the contributions given by the last three Matrons, Miss P. M. Reed, Mrs. Stella Noon and the incumbent Matron, Mrs. Cathy Matthews.

Three Matrons

Stella Noon   *Miss P. M. Reed MBE*   *Cathy Matthews*

photo: Brian Jones

Chapter 10

'Three Matrons'

Miss P. M. Reed is a name already known, by readers of this book.

In an interview with this charming lady 'The real Miss Reed came to life' and her 35 years (plus one month) of life dedicated completely to the Royal Orthopaedic Hospital, is reflected in her philosophy; "I had a feel for orthopaedics, I felt good at it, I felt for the patients and their families". It is in no way surprising that she was subsequently to receive national acclaim and recognition.

Miss Reed (from Leicestershire farming stock, "I had always wanted to be a poultry farmer") commenced her duties on the 1st of September, 1950, on a one year course in Orthopaedic nursing, entering, already having gained qualifications of Midwifery and experience in an Accident hospital in Nottingham. She stayed for 35 years. Miss Mountain, the then Matron, very soon realised her potential making her a ward sister on Ward 6, a permanent sister's post. Miss Reed carried out many duties; including night sister and even as 'stand in' for any absent teacher. The teaching, both at the Woodlands and Forelands schools, was of the very highest standard.

"Exquisite Care" is the term Miss Reed uses for the efficient and friendly atmosphere generated in the hospital at all levels of medical, administrative and domestic staff.

Another consultant surgeon who was greatly admired was Mr. Wilson Stuart, (he was an extra-ordinary surgeon) and he came to mind when Miss Reed recalled the problems that could, and did, arise when some 45 years ago there were no external telephones from the hospital, (except for the private wards). Mr. Stuart rang in for Sister Reed, from an Extern clinic, to inform her that a patient was being sent in. By the time she had made her way to the telephone he had rung off (assuming that the message would have been passed on). It wasn't, and within a very short time she was faced with a patient she was not expecting. A formal request, through the normal channel, no doubt couched with Miss Reed's very strong conviction, regarding the incident was turned down. Mr. Wilson Stuart was therefore approached direct by Sister Reed; subsequent to which a telephone system was installed.

Broad Street was the administration centre there being but one secretary at the Woodlands, Mrs. Marjorie Bierman, who was responsible for all of the office work for the surgeons, matron and hospital staff. She worked with Miss Reed until retirement..

Miss Reed was appointed Assistant Matron in 1962, and Matron, following the retirement of Miss Galbraith, in 1969 and was therefore the last to hold the title 'Matron'. Being a Founder member of the Nurses League in 1965, Miss Reed held the post of Honorary Secretary for 13 years. The League of Friends, formed in 1974, was another of her interests, and she was involved with the production of the newsletters. Despite some early misgivings there was no drop in donations from the 'Brummies' who as Miss Reed says " Took the Royal Orthopaedic to their Hearts" adding also "The pride with which a patient (or family) would say our Fred is a Royal Cripple". (An endearing term long since unacceptable).

"Forelands was far ahead of its time" Miss Reed continues " Its School; its superb teachers; its training facilities." Training in carpentry, splint-making, sewing and the making of padding for leg-irons, etc., being absolutely invaluable, not only to the patient but also to the Hospitals'; Woodlands, Broad Street.(with its Typing school)., which employed so many of them. Miss Reed showed a glowing pride when she said "and surely there is nobody better to make a splint than one who wears one?"

Returning to the first paragraph above, Miss P. M. Reed never faltered in her efforts to improve the training facilities for nurses. Initially she conducted nurse's examinations, from which she moved on to the Panel of Examiners, travelling literally all over the country to centres holding examinations. Just as Miss Mountain had, so the British Orthopaedic Association & Central Council for the Care of Cripples (B.O.A. & C.C.C.C), very soon saw her potential and invited her to join them. Following which she joined R.A.D.A.R., The Royal Association for Disability and Re-habilitation, as an Orthopaedic Nurse Advisor.

The Chairman was an Orthopaedic Consultant and when he resigned Miss Reed, in her own words, "could not have even thought that she would be asked to take the chairmanship", but she was, and held the post until the demise of the movement in the late 1980s. An awe inspiring event which gave her much pleasure was, following her appointment, to go to the Mansion House, London, address the assembled multitude and give the vote of thanks to 'The Lord Mayor of London."

The accolade of course, surely an inevitability, was the award of the M.B.E. presented by Her Majesty Queen Elizabeth, at Buckingham Palace. "For Services to the Orthopaedic Movement"

Thank you Miss P. M. Reed, M.B.E.

Mrs. Stella Noon nee Moseley, was appointed, as Head of Nursing and Patient Services, the second change of title, following Miss Reed's retirement, October 1985. This was a natural step particularly in view of the fact that Stella had started her nursing career as a 16 year old in 1952 at the Woodlands on a two year nursing course, at which time, in referring to Sister Reed, Stella says "I first met and worked under this amazing lady". Stella was amongst a number of the student nurses to transfer for a four year course to the University College Hospital, London (1954-58), the then Matron Miss Mountain having herself joined the Woodlands, from the U.C.H.L. had set up the programme.

Stella then had an 18 year break from the hospital, bringing up her family, and initially moving into school nursing, in Wolverhampton, returning to the Woodlands in 1976.

I returned to Woodlands in 1976 to work as a research nurse for a Medical Research Council 3 year investigation into infections in hip joint replacements - an authoritative multi-centre trial of some 8,000 patients throughout the country. In 1979 I became the 'Control of Infection Sister' to South Birmingham Health Authority.

I moved to Broad Street Outpatients Department as Nursing Officer in Charge until 1985 when I became acting Senior Nursing Officer at Woodlands taking over from Miss Reed and I was appointed to the post a few months later - retiring in March 1991.

My time at Woodlands was always happy and very rewarding I was proud to have begun my career as a student there and to have returned to finish my career there at the top of my profession. The last five years of my time there saw a period of great change the Management Structure throughout the Health Authority changed. The hospital became part of the Acute Unit with the Accident hospital and Selly Oak. We had to become more aware of commercial factors and use of our services. A "bed manager" was appointed to supervise the use of beds sometimes conflicting with consultant colleagues. A new culture was started in the health care and the drive to greater efficiency was beginning.

The hospital received a considerable amount of money to help to reduce our waiting lists, particularly for hip replacements - a target we achieved resulting from great co-operation on everyone's part. Central funding was obtained for the Bone Tumour Service which had been a considerable strain on the Local Health Authority. One of the effects was that we had a dedicated ward for our Bone-Tumour patients - incidentally a ward that was built in 1917 as temporary accommodation until 'something better' could be provided and which has recently (1997) been upgraded for the 4th time. During this 5 year period clinical grading for nurses was introduced - a traumatic time for all.

The hospitals survival became threatened with the Publication of the Plan for a Healthy Birmingham. Proposals for radical changes to hospital care in Birmingham and a serious possibility that the Woodlands would close. The subsequent 'battles' are well documented in the local press but there followed several years of great uncertainty for everyone involved however the hospital has been saved for the fore'seeable future. In a way it comes of no surprise to me. Those of us that know the hospital love it and I am proud to have worked with such dedicated people and have been part of the Woodlands.

Thank you Stella.

Mrs. Catherine A. Matthews is of course the present holder of the position of Matron, sorry Cathy, Business Manager and Director of Nursing

Services (there have been so many changes of names) but, as Cathy says "whatever they call me, I'm still the Matron", a true measure of the friendliness of this quiet, effervescent and efficient lady.

Cathy was appointed in 1967, by the Matron, Miss P. M. Reed, to undertake a twelve month Course in Orthopaedic Nursing. This she found most stimulating as it enabled her to gain the skills to nurse orthopaedic patients. During this period, Cathy recalls that Staff Nurses were the minority in the hospital, so some working full-time found themselves acting as a practitioner for the Ward Areas, checking drugs.

From April 1968 to 1973, Cathy was Ward Sister on Ward 6, Male Orthopaedics, another stimulating and interesting period, overlooking the New Theatres which had been commissioned in 1970. In 1973 she was transferred to the School of Nursing, as a qualified and keen Ward Sister, and during the period to 1981, the standard of the nurses passing through the school in the clinical field, was very high resulting in a 100% pass rate. "The best results in the Country". Results being due to the Student's ability and the 'team determination' both in the school and wards.

Cathy returned to the main hospital (Woodlands) in 1981 as a Nurse Manager, bringing with her a fresh concept to Management, continuing to develop nursing and ensuring a high 'Quality of care' was delivered. With the Bone Tumour team, nurses were sent to be trained in oncology to gain New skills in delivery. New Technology was introduced to assist in accurate administration of chemotherapy, and a ward was erected specially for the benefit of patients care by skilled nurses.

In 1986 Cathy also became the Manager for the Outpatient department at Broad Street, which was eventually transferred back to the main site in October 1993. Following the retirement of Stella Noon, Cathy became the Director of Nursing in 1992. The following three years were "traumatic I found it quite pressurised and it was important to keep Staff Moral, support the team that was working to save the hospital and ensure that the operation aspect continued in that the financial resources audit was complete, showing that we were viable".

Cathy is now able to look at the early developments of the newly appointed NHS Trust Hospital:

New staff were appointed: It now has a Chairman and Chief Executive with the Director of Nursing as one of the Board of Directors, "I continue to be operational, ensuring the nurses are academically prepared to provide the 'Quality of Care' and manage their Budgets. The E.D.U. Ward has a 'Sister', now called 'Ward Manager'.

The hospital is now in the process of building new theatres and is going from strength to strength. As at 1996 the Orthopaedic Nursing Course takes place at two Universities, and is known as ENB 219. There are Nurses in the Trust with the Masters Degree in Advance Nursing Practice.

"When I arrived at the Royal Orthopaedic Hospital, I said I would stay twelve months, but it was such a friendly place, with patients receiving such a high quality of care, I knew that this speciality was for me. I have enjoyed every minute of my time here".

Thank you Cathy, we wish you continued success.

Here we have had the privilege of hearing the stories of three successive Matrons of the Royal Orthopaedic Hospital. Their time with the hospital overlaps, Stella and Cathy have followed in the footsteps of Miss P. M. Reed, both of whom have spoken so highly of the lead given by Miss Reed.

The hospital has been blessed with the highest degree of caring, nurtured by its Matrons'. We are most fortunate to have been able to bring the last Three together.

Chapter 11

The New Era
The Royal Orthopaedic Hospital NHS Trust.

Two letters set the tone of the new era, both from the League of Friends Autumn 1995 Newsletter.

Firstly Mr. Andrew Thomas, Medical Director writes to John Sims:-

"At the last Medical Staff Committee of the Royal Orthopaedic Hospital, I was asked ... to write and personally thank the very many people who helped us on the long and difficult road to achieving Trust status for the Royal Orthopaedic Hospital.

Some people's help was very public and other individuals helped us very much behind the scenes. I do not think we would have achieved Trust status without delivering the amount of clinical work which we did last year and therefore a great deal of the credit must go to the ordinary staff of the hospital who worked so hard.

We also received an unprecedented amount of support from the general public which I am sure was also critical. The fact that so many members of the public supported us is, I think, a reflection of the fact that over the years thousands of people have had operations done or been treated at the Woodlands and by and large they have been pleased with the service which they received.

The Royal Orthopaedic Hospital Board is now in place under the chairmanship of Mr. Bob Jones. We were one of the first Trusts to advertise publicly for members of the Trust Board making this gesture towards openness before it became compulsory. The non-executive directors we have appointed, in my view, bring a very significant expertise to the organisation. Our University nominee, Professor I. Scott, is likely to be very helpful in facilitating the appointment of a Professor of Orthopaedic Surgery.

In terms of the clinical work that we do, the Trust is pressing ahead with appointments of new consultants in arthroscopy and joint reconstruction and in spinal surgery. We have also reached an agreement with the Birmingham Children's Hospital on the future direction of children's orthopaedic services.

The Trustees of the Research and Teaching Centre are forging ahead with an appeal for a children's orthopaedic assessment centre which will, I believe, further consolidate our expertise in this area".

The second is a message from the, then, League of Friends Chairman, Michael Cadbury:-

"The Woodlands has given long years of service in many guises, from the original Cripple's Hospital to the Royal Orthopaedic, at first independent, then part of the National Health Service and finally with the National Health Service Trust status. Throughout the years there has always been a small group of dedicated helpers concerned to have as its objective the welfare of patients and support for the work of nurses and indeed of all staff.

The League of Friends welcomes the hospital's own status and wishes to reiterate its ongoing interest in staff and patients. Our role is unchanged. It has been tempting at various times to get involved in the politics of the situation. We have sought to retain the unique identity of the Woodlands whilst remaining apolitical. We know how much the beautiful grounds and the family atmosphere have meant to patients. We know too how the dedicated teams of surgeons, doctors and nurses have developed and we have campaigned to keep these together.

The publicity generated by open meetings and the many signatures of Friends and supporters have undoubtedly helped to make clear to the powers that be the very wide support for the Woodlands to stay together.

I would like to thank the organisers of the many sided effort to keep the Woodlands intact and to wish the new regime every success in building on the pioneer work developed at the hospital over the years. Our particular thanks for the wide range of financial support enjoyed by the Woodlands. Our League would be grateful for continuing help in its work".

Such introductions are an excellent base from which to look at the progress of the Royal Orthopaedic Hospital NHS Trust during the following two years, this being seen through, primariliy, the columns of the Cutting

Edge Newsletter, its first issue being Winter 1995/96.

The Trusts Chairman needs little introduction, readers of this history having already met 'Master Bobby Jones' in Chapter 8. A distinguished local engineer and industrialist, he had taken on many trouble-shooter roles. Quote: " The Trust is fortunate to have Bob Jones as its Chairman. He values the great achievements of past and present, faces up to change, is prepared to fight for what he believes in and above all is willing to lead. Bob says he enjoys his interests and sport (he watches Aston Villa) but the greatest interest of his life has been his work which he clearly relishes". Unquote.

I wish on a personal note, to give my thanks to Bob Jones, who so kindly gave me an interview, and provided those memories of his early days as a patient at Woodlands. The enthusiasm with which he declared that, when offered a choice of Trust Posts, he had no doubt where his loyalties lay, it must be the Woodlands. Clearly Bob was taking that return Tram journey, without being under duress.

The Chief Executive Neil Taylor took up his post on January 1st, 1995 and on the 23rd March he informed the hospital staff that the Department of Health had given Trust status to the hospital from the 1st April 1995. . To Neil I also give my thanks for coming to my aid when I was searching for post 1970 material for this history.

Neil was again reporting, in the Autumn 1995 Newsletter of the League of Friends (information also from the Winter 1995/96 Cutting Edge), the recent developments:- A Second M.R.I. Scanner (the first NHS hospital in Birmingham to have two scanners) at a cost of £178,000 had been bought from the hospital budget. Its advantage being that it required no building work. To be in operation from 1st September 1995, this new, smaller, scanner would be used for scanning sections of patients' arms and legs, especially knees. In 1994 the hospital had performed 997 joint replacements. Hip replacements recently carried out on a 96 year old pateint and a 12 year old child.   Mr. John O'Hara and Mr. Phil Glithero had joined the medical staff as orthopaedic surgeons in paediatrics, and the annual total of Outpatients treated was 30,000, an anticipated reduction in waiting times to six months by the beginning of 1996 was the aim.

Woodlands School on Ward 11. 1997
photo: Brian Jones

*Miss D. Bennett giving a music lesson
at the Woodlands Hospital Special School. dated 24 June 1971.*
copyright: Birmingham Post & Mail

League of Friends, Gardening Club 1997
Pride in their work
Source: Medical Illuustration, University of Birmingham NHS Trust

The League of Friends Escort service came into being on the 12th June 1996. and the 'Proof is in the Eating', is the Cutting Edge Headline, with Andy Hill (he of the first protest petition fame) and Chris Smith, Head and Assistant Chefs, and their catering colleagues. providing the high culinary standards, catering for 96,000 patient and staff meals each year, serving on average 240 breakfasts, 500 lunches and 175 suppers each week.

Quality Reports; Developing Customer-focused Services; a Boost for Outpatients and Sign Posting to help people find their way around the hospital all have a part in the informative Cutting Edge. There was an interesting article on the Woodlands Hospital School, on Ward 11, by Ann Brown, the then, Headteacher, at Summer 1996. The final paragraph of which is indicative of the professional care of the hospital's teaching staff. 'There may be a change of structure ... but there certainly will not be any change to educational provision made for the children. As long as there are children here we will continue to try and make their hospital experience as positive as possible, preserving a school environment and easing the return to their normal school - life ...".

Ann Weaver, Manager, Research and Teaching Centre, talks of the good progress of the Appeal for the Children's Assessment Centre, in November 1996, and in the same newsletter the Trust has been 'Reaching Out' in a move to take services closer to patients, establishing satellite outpatient clinics in Solihull, Smethwick, and Droitwych. (I recall not so many years before the use of Extern clinics!). How would you have liked a 2 day trip to Calais via Le Shuttle on Saturday 23rd November 1996? The Woodlands Travel Club would have been happy to oblige. I say would have been, because I was booked to go but only 2 days before the tunnel was closed because of a fire.

The 19 members Woodlands Gardening Club were looking for enthusiasts to 'adopt a flower bed, Tools, plants and fertilisers will be provided. All that is required of you is hoeing and keeping your bed tidy'. Dr. Graham Brown was to take up his post of Orthopaedic Physician in October, and Gail Aspley her post of Domestic Supervisor. Dina Penrose, the Head Occupational Therapist retired on the 17th November after 17 years service with the ROH. Also leaving were Sue Byfield, Pharmacy

Clerk and Denise Burke, General Finance Assistant.

The front page of the Winter 1996/7 Cutting Edge is devoted to the Chief Executive's three phase Site Development plans at the ROH.

Phase One: Physiotherapy and Occupational Therapy having moved into new accommodation; Orthotics, Pharmacy, Medical Records and X-ray Storage to move to improved accommodation; The Linen Room and Occupational Therapy Storage to move into the area vacated by the Back Pain Clinic, and the Social Work Department to swap accommodation with the Spinal Surgeons and Secretaries.

Second phase: The Sub-station being built at the back of the hospital will provide significantly more electricity: Work to start on new Operating Theatres and new Outpatient Department, the latter within Phase three comes within a Business Plan forwarded to the Regional Office for the complete development of the site, the Outpatients Department moving to the top of the site, where presently Wards 11 and 12 are, together with X-ray, Physiotherapy etc. All the wards moving to areas surrounding the Operating Theatres and will be completely new. The latter phase being projected to be timed for the turn of the century.

Spring 1997 announces that the ROH is to apply to the Charter Mark Unit to be judged against their standards, and gives examples of how the Charter Mark criteria are being met within the ROH departments.

I summarise the nine main areas.

The nursing department has introduced four generic clinical standards -

1. Pain management. Pressure area care. Discharge management, The named nurse.

2. Information & openness; The X-ray Department tested how good the information was that patients were receiving, and the High Dependency Unit is to audit how well patients are advised prior to undergoing surgery.

3. Consultation & Choice; The Catering Department working closely with Ward Managers to ensure that the menus reflect patients choice ...

4. Courtesy & Helpfulness 'Welcome' notices in all Wards, enabling visitors to identify the staff. Physiotherapy staff attending quality training days to improve awareness of staff/customer relations.

5. Putting Things Right; patients and visitors receiving a complaints

leaflet.

6. Value for Money; The introduction of a telephone booking system in the Day Ward, so reducing the number of cancellations.

7. User Satisfaction; All departments encouraged to have a questionnaire.

8. Measurable Improvements; More operations. More patients. More activity.

9. Service Enhancement - at no extra cost.

With reference to the latest Summer 1997 Cutting Edge the 1997/98 Business Plan Developments include:

Improving Patient Care and Facilities; Our Commitment to Local Services; Further Development of Spinal Services; Our Commitment to Leading Developments in Orthopaedic Treatment. and - Orthopaedic Services into the Next Millennium.

"The Trust has progressed plans for a major redevelopment of the Northfield site. This will greatly improve the environment for patients providing new ward accommodation, dedicated day case unit, rehabilitation and high dependency facilities. The major management agenda for 1997/98 is to secure the investment required for the site redevelopment."

I have to say that the information coming out of the 'Cutting Edge' is not only of great interest, but in terms of the sources of minutes, reports etc. from which this history has been put together, at no stage have I had such clarity of detail. It is particularly noticeable in terms of the description of proposed modifications on the ROH site.

Mr. John Churchman kindly responded to my request for an historical look at the work of the X-ray Department over the last 30 years. I am most grateful for these 'inside views'. Throughout the last 100 years I have referred briefly to the work of particular men who contributed to the development of X-rays. Mr. Hall-Edwards and Dr. Brailsford being but two. From John's material we can look at the improvements during the last three decades with particular reference to the Royal Orthopaedic Hospital.

With patients no longer coming from Forelands to be x-rayed, links with the Victoria Special School in Northfield had resulted in their children coming to Woodlands for x-rays. Facilities had improved, with the number of x-ray rooms increasing from one to three, an increase in the number of theatres and a resulting need for more radiographers to assist the surgeons with imaging during operations.

The department had taken delivery of its first mobile image intensifier in 1980, an x-ray set linked to a television monitor, giving a live and dynamic image of the area being examined. The decision of the Health Authority to close, at very short notice, the Broad Street Outpatients Department, had an immediate and great effect on the X-ray Department, not only reducing the number of rooms available for all work from five to three, but also the Woodlands X-ray Department which had hitherto dealt almost exclusively with inpatients, had within a few weeks to deal with the large number of outpatients.

Staff had responded both to the needs of the patients and the hospital by introduction of an on-call system, to cover nights and weekends, by staffing evening clinics and adapting departmental opening hours. Regular surveys of the views of patients are carried out, and acted on wherever possible. Other changes reflect clinical and technological developments, some of their investigations being carried out by other kinds of imaging. The department had ultrasound while 'up the corridor' are the two MRI scanners. However, x-ray examinations are far from having lost their usefulness. The differing imaging methods should rather be thought of as complementing each other, each having its distinctive contribution to the diagnosis and assessment of a patient.

In addition to their ability to show fine bone detail, one of the great strengths of x-rays as an imaging method is their versatility; patients can be easily examined while in bed, and on the ward if it is difficult to move them to the X-Ray Department. X-ray examinations have now risen to more than 20,000 annually.

In terms of moving with the times, and developing of techniques, we read that 30 years ago six porters would have been needed to help lift patients with TB of the spine out of the plaster bed on which they would have to lie for months, (see Robert Christie's comments in Chapter 8 Memories), in order that they could be x-rayed. Nowadays, radiographers x-ray patients in order, for example, to provide accurate measurements for medical engineers to construct replacements for bones with tumours in them, or to enable spinal surgeons to measure and assess deformities such as abnormal curvature of the spine. A single cassette used for these specialised techniques may cost more that £3,000.

Wet processing has given way to automatic processors. At the same time, staff have continually sort to address radiation safety issues by updating equipment, reviewing practice and refining techniques.

Among the many long serving members of staff have been Philip Jacobs, Consultant Radiologist, (previously referred to), and Sheila Binns, Superintendent Radiographer, who each were in post for a quarter of a century. The increasing workload has meant that two Consultant Radiologists now serve the hospital.

An X-ray Department Update, article provided by Mr. Steve Barlow, Senior 1. Radiographer, in the Summer 1997 Cutting Edge, comments on the continuous striving to enhance the x-ray service, and the friendly and professional attitude of the staff. During the last twelve months the department had been completely redecorated and the reception areas improved. The filming area had been extended and three major new items of equipment purchased, a Siemens Siremobil Image Intensifier; An Aloka SSD 2000 Ultrasound machine ,and, A Kodak M35 processor has replaced the wet processing tanks.

The department has extended its opening hours with the X-ray office opening at 8.30 am. each day, and a bank of radiographers are providing cover for evening clinics, Day Ward screening lists and Sunday opening to reduce Monday morning waiting times. Quality improvements have been made in response to patients requests. Joint replacement patients are now x-rayed on route between HDU and the ward so reducing the number of times the patient has to be moved.

Finally Mr. Barlow informs patients that the X-ray service is provided by the University Hospitals Birmingham NHS Trust. There staff having worked as hard for, and are as much part of the ROH as any of us.

A Progress Report, March 1997, produced as a pamphlet, enables us to look at the ROH NHS Trust achievements to date, Further developments 1997 and Orthopaedic Services into the Next Millennium.

The Chairman's Message being:-

"As a member of the general public you are entitled to be referred to whichever medical practitioner you wish. Obviously your General Practitioner is in an informed position about who is most appropriate, but the Royal Orthopaedic NHS Trust provides all forms of orthopaedic care and is a premier provider of this service for the Birmingham conurbation."

Achievements in 1996/7

.. Reduction in waiting times.

.. 11% more patients treated.

.. Rationilisation of Therapy

.. Purchased second MRI Scanner for single limb scans.

.. Improved information for patients.

.. New Electrical Sub Station to enable further development of hospital services, particularly increasing numbers of operating theatres and X-ray capacity.

.. Established a clinical Unit to assess the effectiveness of surgical treatments in conjunction with Birmingham University.

.. Launched a Public Appeal for a new

Further Developments of the Royal Orthopaedic Hospital 1997

.. Three new operating theatres, making the ROH the largest Orthopaedic centre in the UK.

.. Upgrading Outpatients Department.

.. Child Assessment Centre Services.

..Upgrade League of Friends Coffee Shop.

.. Increased car parking.

Children's Assessment Unit.

.. Voluntary help increased by 200%.

.. Increased car parking.

Orthopaedic Services into the Next Millennium

.. New Outpatient Department.

.. New X-ray Department.

.. New Wards.

.. New Private Patient Unit.

.. Additional car parking.

The Largest Orthopaedic Centre in the West Midlands

Each year the Trust performs approximately:

1000 hip and knee joint replacements.

600 knee arthroscopies.

1000 operations on children.

1600 spinal operations.

600 emergency operations

The hospital is at the leading edge of developments in orthopaedic treatments and provides highly specialised care for a national, regional and local population. As a world renownwed Orthopaedic Centre highly specialised treatments are undertaken:

.. Life saving surgical treatment of patients with primary bone tumours.

.. Corrective surgery for patients with spinal deformities.

.. Corrective surgery for limb length inequality. Corrective surgery for young adults with hip dysplasia.

.. Complex surgery for patients with failed or worn out primary hip and knee replacements.

.. Instrumental Intervertebral fusions following removal of secondary tumours in the spine.

.. Corrective surgery for congenital hand abnormalities.

The Fact File gives the statistics:

	95/96	96/97
Inpatients treated	7,838	8,556
Outpatients treated	33,918	37,994
Consultant Medical staff	26	30

The Birmingham Evening Mail once again gives its support to the Royal Orthopaedic Hospital NHS Trust with a 'full colour centre page spread' on Wednesday, November 20, 1996. in which Neil Taylor the Hospital's Chief Executive states 'Our Impressive record on efficiency, looking at 'Striving for Excellence' and 'The Future', as the Royal Orthopaedic Hospital celebrated its first year as an NHS Trust. In the main the above stated Progress Report encompasses most that Neil had to say. There is however one section referring to the Voluntary Services provided by the League of Friends., on which I would like to make comment.

Over the years the role of the voluntary helpers may have changed, today we are not talking of the Linen League, Visitors, Collectors, Band of Help, P.S.A's etc. all of whom laid the foundation of the hospital's success. Today the volunteers are the 'Gardener's', 'Escort's', 'Clerical and Administrative assistance', and 'the Running of the coffee shop'. Added to which is all the assistance provided at Open Days and Fetes. The Woodlands Travel Club Ltd. of course being not only a major source of money raising, but also giving great pleasure to its traveller's.

This brings this history of the Orthopaedic Hospital up to date and to an end except for two things. The opening of the first Institute 180 years ago was accompanied by the list of 'men' who had the foresight to form the orthopaedic movement. At each stage of development I have stated the lists of changing committees, it is therefore important that I provide details of the latest list of the 'men and women' both professional and volunteers, who are today taking those ideals into the 21st century.

Coordinator of Volunteers, Mr. Arthur McKeown.

League of Friends Committee

President: Michael H. Cadbury

Chairman: Roland B. Treacy

Hon. Secretary: Peter Jubb

Hon. Treasurer: Bill Goodman

Annette Dicker; Peter Dixon; Leslie Fennell; Bob Fischer; Mary Iwanicki; John McAndrew; Brenda Parkes; Jack Payne; John Sims; Ken Turner.

Research & Teaching Centre

Contact - Ann Weaver

Christine Hames; Nesta Jenkins; Georgina Maycey; Eric Rolls.

Stocktaking

Contact - Bill Goodman. Ken Bancroft; Hilda Sims

Escorts

Contact - John McAndrew

Gwen Brendreth; Brenda Colwell; Myra Dean; Peter Dixon, Sheila Fennell; Trevor Gibbs; Bob Hawkesford; Joan Hill, Ernest Jones; John McAndrew; Ivy Morris; Bill Thomas, Veronica Thomas; Ken Turner.

Gardening Club

Contact - John Sims

Ruth Bailey; Billy Baird; Peter Butler; Ralph Clark; George Davis, Gwen Fogarty; Bob & Romola Grainger; David Hunter; Ernest Jones, Brian & Yvonne Lee; Mac & Sheila McLaren; John Medding, Dina Penrose; Ken Spurrier; Bob & Sue Watkins; Connie White.

Coffee Shop

Contact - Wendy Cochrane

Audrey Adams; Mary Carr; Barbara Evans; Margaret Fleming, Margaret Giles; Kathleen Grosvenor; Margaret Hanson; Brenda Harris Hazel Heaton; Lilian Hewitt; Joyce Hobbins; Mary Iwanicki, June Jones; Barry & Dot Judd; Pat Lewis; Gaby Madden, Brenda Mann; Iris Mason; Lily Malyn; Marion May, John & Pat Peduzzi; Lyn Sharp; Cherry Styler; Winifred Swan,

Connie Taylor; Evelyn Timms; Brenda Wall; Irene Wetherall,
Iris Wilson.
Volunteer Support Members
Contact - Peter Dixon
Margaret Adkins; Bill Bailey; Margaret Brownley; Barbara Butcher,
Eileen Davis; John Davis; Rene Dowler; Bob & Pauline Fischer,
John Gardiner; Jean Glover; Brian & Olive Jones; Sheila Lacey,
Dora Lee; Colin & Margaret Patrick; Phillip & Pat Potter,
Jean Ravenhill; Patricia Smart; Ken Spurrier; Mary White,
Jackie Wickham; Iris Wilson.
Sale of Christmas Cards Stella Noon.

The Royal Orthopaedic Hospital NHS Trust staffing as at 11 June 1997.

Management and Administrative.

		Number of staff in the team
Mr. N. Taylor	Chief Executive	9. including Chairman, Secretary 6 Non-Executive Directors + 1 for Histopathology.
Mr. G. F. Bragg	Director of Finance and Information	12.
Mrs. C. Matthews	Director of Nursing	254. includes Admin. Staff & all nursing staff.
Mr. G. Hyland	Business Planning & Contracting Manager.	5.
Mrs. Dalloway	Therapy Services Manager	27.
Mrs. Barrett/ Ms. S. Brennan	Senior Social Workers	6.
Mrs. P. Prince	Head Occupational Therapist	6.

Mr. A. Mitchell	Head of Facilities	13.
Mrs. S. MacArthur	Superintendent Radiographer	15.
Mrs. E. Leung	Head Pharmacist	5.
Miss L. Pye	Administrator, Birmingham Orthopaedic Oncology Service	11.includes Mr.R.Grimes & Mr. S. Larter
Mrs. A. Baxter	Headmistress, Woodlands School	5.
Mr. D. Adams	Portering/Security Manager	14.
Mr. C. Hitchens	Health Records Manager	41.
Ms. A. Saunders	Superintendent Radiographer - MRI Centre	15.
Miss A. Weaver	Administrator, Research & Teaching Centre	3 + 3.
Mr. J. Sharpe	Hotel Services Manager	58.
Mrs. M. Fogg	Personnel Officer	2.
Mr. A. Thomas	Medical Director	41.
Dr. C. Thomas	Consultant Anaesthetist	9.
	Total	554.

Consultants

	Specialty
Mr. C. F. Bradish	Children's Orthopaedics including Limb Lengthening
Dr. G. J. Brown	Back Pain and Sports Medicine
Mr. S. Carter	Orthopaedic Oncology and Joint Replacement Surgery
Mr. P. R. Clithero	Children's Orthopaedics including Neuromuscular Problems

Dr. I. Green	General Physician
Mr. R. Grimer	Orthopaedic Oncology and General Orthopaedics
Mr. D. J. A. Learmonth	Arthroscopy Surgery, Knee & Shoulder Reconstruction
Miss R. Lester	Plastic Surgery
Mr. D. S. Marks	Spinal Deformities
Mr. P. Mulligan	Hand Surgery
Dr. T. Neal	Anaesthetics
Mr. J. N. O'Hara	Children's Orthopaedics including hip dysplasia
Mr. J. Plewes	Foot Surgery and Joint replacement Surgery
Mr. A. J. Stirling	Spinal Surgery
Mr. A. M. C. Thomas	Rheumatoid Joint Replacements
Mr. C. Thomas	Anaesthetist
Mr. A. G. Thompson	Spinal Deformities
Mr. R. M. Tillman	Orthopaedic Oncology and Joint Replacement Surgery
Mr. R. B. Treacy	Primary and Revision Joint Replacement Surgery
Mr. O. N. Tubbs	Knee Surgery
Mr. M. A. Waldram	Hand Surgery

It is worth looking back through the 180 years, by noting the 'Photograph Gallery' on display in the Research and Teaching Centre today (1997). The Hospital Committee had, as has been reported earlier in this history, been looking to providing such a gallery, shortly after its considerations re the 'Board for Surgeons etc.'

George Freer. 1817 - 1829.

George Fabion Evans. M.D. 1836 - 1873.

Thomas Bell Elcock Fletcher. M.D., F.R.C.P. 1873 - 1894.

Sir. Gilbert Barling. F.R.C.S. 1884 - 1886.

Frank Barnes. F.R.C.S. 1904 - 1918.

F. Victor Milward. F.R.C.S. 1908 - 1910.

Jordan Lloyd. F.R.C.S. 1908 - 1914.

Mr. Naughton Dunn. M.A., M.B., ChB., LL.D.

Surgeon Royal Orthopaedic Hospital. 1913 - 1939.

C. Percival Mills. F.R.C.S. 1912 - 1946.

F. Wilson Stewart. M.D., Ch.M. 1917 - 1954.

Mr. James F. Brailsford. 1923 - 1956.

T. S. Donovan. M.Ch.Orth., F.R.C.S. 1939 - 1966.

F. G. Allan. F.R.C.S. 1939 - 1966.

Max Harrison. M.Ch.Orth., F.R.C.S. 1958 - 1987.

Mr. C. Paul Cotterill. 1963 - 1987.

Mr. Robert F. N. Duke. 1969 - 1986.

Mr. Jeremy C. T. Fairbank. 1985 - 1989.

Mr. William H. Scrase. 1956 - 1977.

It must be noted that the dates and Professional Qualifications stated are those actually on the Gallery Photographs on display. It is clearly not a complete statement of all members of the Medical Staff, either of today or over the 180 years. All names of course appear on the official notice boards. (see photograph).

Second and as a final comment, whether looking at the Cripple's Union or the Orthopaedic Hospital, throughout this history there have been many examples of expressions of appreciation showered upon them. The Royal OrthopaedicHospital NHS Trust is no exception as these two letters show:

"It was in 1993 that life really began to change for me. On holidays hills became mountains to climb, hobbies more difficult to follow. Too painful to sit all day at a cricket match or all evening at the theatre - and, considering myself to still be in the prime of life in my early sixties thought "is this all that is left to me from now on?" Eventually I visited my G.P. was referred to an orthopaedic consultant who diagnosed an arthritic hip, placed on a waiting list for surgery and eventually admitted to the Woodlands Hospital for total hip replacement.

Considering the demands on the hospital the waiting time was not excessive and from the consultant Mr. S. Carter, his team, nursing and ward staff, auxiliaries and members of staff in outpatients I received nothing but kindness, consideration and first class care. Now nearly 18 months after the operation what a joy it is to be free of that agonising pain and resume hobbies, including gardening, grandchildren and once more sit all day at a cricket match. For me no amount of thanks could ever repay that hospital and its staff."

This was written by Mrs. Valerie Barnwell from Moseley

And Val's husband Mr. Jack Barnwell also has reasons for thanking the Woodlands;

"I have arthritis in both knees, and following a routine check at the rheumatology clinic at Selly Oak Hospital I was referred to Woodlands for hydrotherapy treatment. I did not have to wait long for an appointment, and I found the staff at the Woodlands most friendly and helpful. The three week course I was given this year , (1997), with follow-up exercises which I was instructed to do at home, have brought a significant improvement in my mobility."

Postscript

by

Robert N. Jones

Chairman of the
Royal Orthopaedic Hospital
NHS Trust

The Royal Orthopaedic Hospital NHS Trust, as an institution, has always managed to achieve one simple primary goal and that is to do its utmost to treat each patient as an individual and to alleviate them as far as possible from the pain, discomfort and illness from which they may suffer.

The history that this book explains highlights the energy, humanity, dedication and humour that are associated with treating patients and my everlasting memories of the Royal Orthopaedic Hospital, both as a patient in the 1930s and latterly now as the Chairman of the Royal Orthopaedic Hospital NHS Trust, will forever remind me that it is the people that matter and not the politics.

I hope, in one hundred years, that its success in treating patients will have been as interesting and challenging as the previous one.

My thanks go to the author for his insight and ability to highlight both the humorous and the relevant facts that make the Royal Othopaedic Hospital the best Orthopaedic Hospital in the world, but also to many patients, volunteers, relatives and staff who have passed through its doors.

R. N. Jones
Chairman.

Conclusion

The amount of material studied to obtain this history has been great, and of course has required much reduction and editing. The facts stated are as given in 'Minutes', 'Annual Reports' etc, the early years of which were in the main hand written. The interpretation is of course my own, and I hope that no errors have thus resulted. In relation to the spelling of proper nouns there may have been some difficulties in the reading of the handwritten entries, for which I would apologise. I have deliberately not included any possible contentious statements, or comment.

All photographic material has been acknowledged, from the numerous sources. In terms of photographs not carrying 'copy-write' statements which are part of the Royal Orthopaedic Hospital Archive material I wish to thank the Hospital Management for free access, and this includes their permission to use all of their archival material.

Throughout this history I have attempted to provide information which will, in particular, be of interest to anyone who has had contact with the hospital in any way. In other words there should be something of interest to all.

The history will of course be relevant not only to the general reader in terms of the changes and developments of hospital life, but of course, to the 'Historian' and 'Archivist', to that end I have included that initial 'scene setting', 'facts and figures', 'names of surgeons', 'alumni', etc., and by including material, particularly from the 1970's, extracted from quarterly newsletters it has been possible to bring together, for the benefit of all readers, that information previously read by but a limited hospital readership.

The overall acknowledgements for contributions to this history follow, however I feel that I must here express my great appreciation to Bob Jones, Chairman and Neil Taylor, Chief Executive, of the Royal Orthopaedic NHS Trust for allowing me the freedom of hospital access. Also to the numerous current, and past, hospital staff as a whole, too many to name individually, who have given me such support and encouragement. But two that I must separate out are:

Firstly, Michael Cadbury. My appreciation is well known, of the contribution made of the Cadbury family to Birmingham Life, from the time of the arrival in Birmingham in 1794 of Richard Tapper Cadbury (George Cadbury's grandfather). The Cadbury family has been connected with this hospital history from the 1860's without a break. Michael was the first Chairman of the League of Friends (formed December 1974) holding that position until May 3rd 1997 at which date he became its President. (on the retirement of Mr. Jack Payne). It has indeed been my privilege to have, through this book, met Michael, and in thanking him personally for his full support, I would congratulate him, I am sure on everyone's behalf, on his new position, so continuing the family tradition.

Secondly, this history would not have been written, by this author, without the full support and enthusiasm of Mr. John Sims, and of course Sandra. I thank them both most sincerely for their confidence and help through out.

The Royal Orthopaedic Hospital NHS Trust now moves into the 21st Century, no doubt the passage will not always be smooth, this history shows that it never was, but there were always blue skies ahead. One factor however that still rings true today, 1997, is that imbued by the generations of people from the establishment, and subsequent developments over the last 180 years, of the orthopaedic institutions.

That factor being the:

Royal Orthopaedic Hospital the Caring Hospital

Mr. & Mrs. Michael Cadbury
(Aerial Photograph of the Forelands in the Background)

*Mrs. Heather Cadbury. JP. has, of course, also carried the 'Cadbury' tradition
of serving the hospital. Heather having been on the: Rubery Hill and
Hollymoor Hospital Managment
Committee 1961-62 and Selly Oak Hospital Mangement Committee 1962-63.
Both institutions have been seen to have played their role, in this history of the
Royal Orthopaedic Hospital.*

Acknowledgements

To the following, all of whom so kindly assisted the search for information on the story leading up to the gift, by George Cadbury, of the Woodlands to the Cripples Union.

Ivor G. Hamel Cooke; Helen M. Davis, Library and Archives, - Dept. V53, Cadbury Ltd; Mrs. D. Harvey; Bernard Hewlett; Mrs. Moira Wright. Keith Tyler; Fiona Tait, Archivist, Central Library & the Bournville Village Trust Estate Office; Lloyds Bank, Bournville & University of Birmingham, Branches.

For their kindness in allowing the chapter on -

Mr. Naughton Dunn.

Mr. Peter M. Dunn, MA., MD., FRCP., FRCOG., FRCPCH.

Emeritus Professor of Perinatal Medicine and Child Health

Mr. Max Harrison, M.Ch.Orth.,FRCS.

To the members of the Research & Teaching Centre for their help and forbearance -

Mrs. Doreen Smith who opened up the Library each morning and swept around me. Judy Dawson, Archivist. Dr. P. B. Pensent. Ph.D.

Ann Weaver. Carol Morris. Nesta Jenkins.

To Amanda Littlewood and the 'Cutting Edge' editorial team..

To the late Mr. Alan Billing, for setting out the ground rules for this history, and Mrs. Margaret Scott who, over the years, has carried out so much research on the hospital.

Mr. Roy Calfield for his information on the Chadwick End 'Woodlands' Convalescent Cottage Home.

Winnie Wort, and Kath. Watts for the Cripples Union details particularly on Mr.A.E.Wort and the Workmen's Auxiliary Committee.

Mr. Sydney Caro. MBE, Trevor Hancock, and the 'Rocket Club'.

John Churchman for his help re the X-ray update.

Ann Brown and Ann Baxter, for information on the Woodlands School.

Andy Mitchell. Jim Pendry for access to the attic.

Miss Joyce Clark for information re the Methodist Church services.

Miss P. M. Reed. MBE. Stella Noon. Cathy Matthews.

Acknowledgements

Austin Moseley. Nesta Jenkins. Michael Cadbury. Bob Jones. Neil Taylor. Andy Hill. Revd. David Collyer. Jack Payne.

To the many members of the League of Friends who have offered advice, and to Brian Jones in particular who has so kindly given so much effort to tramping the corridors and the grounds of the hospital taking photographs. His enthusiasm and effort being quite infectious.

To Mr. Ian Dowell, Editor of the Birmingham Mail, for giving permission for the use of copyright photographs from their collection. I would also like to express my thanks to Mr. Mike Evetts of the Mail staff for his invaluable help in making the material available. I also would give my thanks to Mr. Dowell for taking my article in the Mail, asking for 'peoples memories' re the Orthopaedic Hospital, and re information on Mr. Frank Mathews The response was amazing.

To the following contributors to those 'Memories' I am so grateful:-

Mr. Jack & Mrs. Valerie Barnwell; Mary Birks; Mary Bowers; Mrs. Doreen M. Brownhill; Mr. John Carney; Mr. Robert Christie; Mrs. June Clark; Mr. Ivor Cooke; Mrs. E. A. Cooksey; Mrs. C. A. Corles; Mrs. Susy Crisp; Mr. Eric & Mrs. Peggy Crooks; Mrs. Edith Crow Mrs. D. M. Darby; Mrs. Edna Dawson; Mrs. Sheila Eglinton; Mrs. Dorothy Ellis; Mr. N. H. Field; Mrs. A. Greaves; Mr. Ronald Glover; Mrs. M. Gould; Mrs. Margaret Handley; Mrs. M. J. Hinton; Miss D. Hodgson; Miss J. Jennings; Bob Jones; Mrs. Cherry Lawley; Mr.Michael G. Lee; Mrs. Jean Lynch; Mrs. Hilda Mearden; Mrs. Rosie E. Morton; Mrs. Linda Moss; Mrs. Alice Nicholls; Miss M. Owen; Mrs. Kathleen Pitman; Mrs. N. Playdon; Mr. A. W. Skidmore; Mrs. Sheila Skoczsylas; Mrs. Hilda Taylor. Mr. Brian Troth. Mr. Basil Walker.

To Dr. Carl Chinn and Radio W.M. for 'Air-time'.

In the hope that I have included everybody, I end by giving my thanks to all those people, too numerous to mention, who have given advice along the way.

I must thank my wife Ann for her support and encouragement.

Bibliography

Minute Books - Orthopaedic Hospital

1817 - 1884: 1874 - 1889: 1890 - 1900: 1901 - 1910: 1911 - 1921: 1922 - 1924.

Orthopaedic Developments in Birmingham 1817 - 1947 (2 - A4 sheets)

Royal Orthopaedic & Spinal Hospital

1903 - 1912 (Medical): 1906 - 1912: 1908 - 1914: 1911 - 1921:

1912 - 1918: 1915 - 1925: 1918 -1922: 1922 - 1924: 1915 - 1925.

Annual Reports: 1927 - 1932; 1933 - 1938: 1939 -1947.

Amalgamation: 1924 - 1926: 1924 - 1925: 1927 - 1937.

Cripples Union

March 1899 to May 1900: (Birmingham & District Crippled Children's Union) 1904 - 1909: 1906 - 1914:

Special Sub-Committee 1907 - 1924: 1910 - 1915: 1915 - 1922:

1922 - 1925.

Birmingham (Selly Oak) Hospital Management Committee, The Royal Cripples Hospital, Birmingham, The Woodlands, Northfield.

1909 - 1956.

Royal Cripples Hospital , Reports, 1925 - 1929

Annual Reports 1927 - 1932: 1933 - 1938: 1935 - 1947: 1939 - 1947.

Workmen's Auxiliary Committee

1907 - 1914: 1921 - 1927: Special Sub-Committee 1907 - 1924: 1921 - 1927.

Landmarks in the History of the Woodlands School 1914 - 1996 -

Ann Brown

The Rocket Club. by Olly Hill & Mickie Fraser. 1949.

History of Birmingham 1805 'A Brief History of Birmingham; intended as A Guide to the Inhabitant & Stranger'. Third Edition. (1st Edition 1797, 2nd Edition 1802.)Printed & Sold by Wilkes & Grafton.

Sale Catalogues;

The Woodlands, Thursday July 20th, 1899. (Property of Mr. Ivor G. H. Cooke).

The Forelands Estate, Bromsgrove, Thursday September 25th, 1919. (Royal Orthopaedic Hospital Archives)

Research & Teaching Centre - Folders.

M.R.I. - Folders.

Belmont - Committee Minutes

League of Friends - Minutes & Newsletters

Royal Orthopaedic Hospital 'Cutting Edge' Newsletters

Hydrotherapy Pool - Three Folders

The Royal Orthopaedic Hospital League (Nurses League)

Newsletter 1967

Elizabeth Cadbury - by Richenda Scott.

Life of George Cadbury - by A. G. Gardiner.

The Edwardian Lady - Compiled by Ina Taylor.

Birmingham Theatres, Concerts and Music Halls - Victor J. Price.

Bournville Carillon. Bournville Works Magazines.

A Century of Birmingham Life 1871.- Chronicle of Local events -

1741 - 1841, Volumes 1 & 2. - John Alfred Langford, LL.D.

Old and New Birmingham, 1880 and The Making of Birmingham, 1894 - by
Robert K. Dent.

History of the Free-Schools, Colleges, Hospitals, and Asylums of
Birmingham, 1861- by George Griffith.

1873 - 1973 The Golden Years a Concise History of the Birmingham
Hospital Saturday Fund, - by Mr. E. R. Sherlock.

Newspaper Cuttings - from the R.T.C. Archives.

Publisher's Note

Mr Maurice White, the author of this book has very kindly donated all royalties from the sale of the book to the Royal Orthopaedic Hospital League of Friends in perpetuity.

Nett proceeds from the sale of the first 2,000 copies and the royalties from any further reprints of this book will be received by the Royal Orthopaedic Hospital League of Friends to be used for the benefit of the patients and staff at the Royal Orthopaedic Hospital. Our thanks to the passengers of the Woodlands Travel Club Ltd for making publication possible.